PRACTICAL FIBRE-OPTIC PROJECTS

by

R. A. PENFOLD

BERNARD BABANI (publishing) LTD
THE GRAMPIANS
SHEPHERDS BUSH ROAD
LONDON W6 7NF
ENGLAND

Please Note

Although every care has been taken with the production of this book to ensure that any projects, designs, modifications and/or programs, etc., contained herewith, operate in a correct and safe manner and also that any components specified are normally available in Great Britain, the Publishers do not accept responsibility in any way for the failure, including fault in design, of any project, design, modification or program to work correctly or to cause damage to any other equipment that it may be connected to or used in conjunction with, or in respect of any other damage or injury that may be so caused, nor do the Publishers accept responsibility in any way for the failure to obtain specified components.

Notice is also given that if equipment that is still under warranty is modified in any way or used or connected with home-built equipment then that warranty may be void.

British Library Cataloguing in Publication Data

Penfold, R. A.

Practical Fibre-optic Projects

I. Title

621.3692

ISBN 0 85934 374 X

Printed and bound in Great Britain by Cox & Wyman Ltd, Reading

Preface

It seems as though fibre-optic cables have been about to revolutionise all our lives for many years now! After a few false starts fibre-optic cables are now being threaded around the country, and it looks as though they may bring some major changes in the fields of communications and entertainment over the coming years. Although it is a subject that conjures up visions of hi-tech equipment sending giga-bits of information in a matter of milliseconds, fibre-optics can be used for more mundane tasks such as simple audio and computer data links. Furthermore, cables and other components for home constructed equipment of this type are readily available.

This book provides a number of practical circuits for fibre-optic audio links, data links, and a few other gadgets that make use of fibre-optic cables. The components used are all available to amateur users at reasonable prices, as is the optical cable itself. Chapter 1 provides details of adapting ordinary LEDs and photocells for use with fibre-optic cables. Therefore, if preferred, most of the projects can be constructed without using any special fibre-optic devices. Although this book is not aimed at complete beginners to electronic project construction, several of the circuits are quite simple and should not be beyond the capabilities of someone who has some experience at electronic project construction. These include the simple a.m. audio links, the simple d.c. link, the d.c. data link, the MIDI link, and the d.c. loop alarm.

R. A. Penfold

Contents

Chapter 1

FIBRE-OPTIC BASICS

Fibre-optic cables have been freely available to amateur users for many years now, but surprisingly little practical information about using them in home constructed equipment has so far been published. Fibre-optic cables are capable of transmitting data at a vast rate, but sending giga-bits per second is something that is presumably of littleinterest to amateur users. Being able to send dozens of television signals down a single cable is fine provided you actually have all those signals to send! Presumably most amateur users are interested in sending d.c., audio, and digital signals along fibre-optic cables. Audio and d.c. signals do not require vast bandwidths, even if they are sent in a digitised or semi digitised form. Digital signals could involve greater bandwidths, but here we will only be concerned with signals at ordinary RS232C baud rates that can be handled using inexpensive and readily available components. The serial approach is the only low cost method of sending digital data down a single fibre-optic cable.

Advantages

It would seem reasonable to question the use of fibre-optic cables except where their potential bandwidth of many megahertz is really needed. For most electronic hobbyists it is probably their novelty value that is the main attraction. For someone who is suffering from "seen it all before" syndrome, optical cables offer an interesting new field for experimentation. They are presumably no less interesting for those who are relatively new to the hobby, but like to experiment with the more unusual types of project.

Even ignoring its novelty value, there are some potential advantages in using an optical cable. Perhaps the main one is that fibre-optic cables do not radiate any electrical interference. This can be a major problem with ordinary wire cables, especially when dealing with something like a high speed serial data link. Although the fundamental signal may be at only about 10kHz, the fast switching speed ensures that there are

1

strong harmonics at frequencies many times higher than this. In fact strong harmonics are likely to be present at frequencies of a few megahertz. In order to prevent strong radio frequency interference (r.f.i.) being transmitted from the cable it is normally necessary to use a high quality screened cable. Such a cable is often rather bulky, quite expensive, and may not give complete freedom from this problem. A fibre-optic cable is small, and produces no radio frequency emissions at all due to the fact it is not carrying an electrical signal.

Another problem with conventional cables is that they tend to pick-up radio frequency interference, mains "hum", and all manner of electrical noise. This problem is at its worst with low level audio signals and long cables. However, it can still be quite severe with audio signals at relatively high levels and a connecting cable just a few metres long. Again, a high quality screened cable helps to minimise the problem, but might not completely eliminate it. I suppose that a fibre-optic cable is not guaranteed to be totally free from interference, and light from the outside world could find its way into the cable. In practice the outer sleeving of optical cables is sufficiently opaque to ensure that there is no problem at all with stray pickup.

Conventional screened twin leads can suffer from problems with cross-talk. In other words, an inductive or capacitive coupling can result in the signal in one lead being coupled into the other lead. This problem is mainly associated with audio cables, but it can also occur with multi-way digital cables. In fact severe corruption of the data can sometimes occur with parallel data links, even if quite short cables are used. In theory it is possible for cross-talk to occur with a twin optical cable, but in reality there is no problem of this type. Even with a very long twin cable there is no significant light coupling from one fibre to the other. Blocking light is much easier than blocking an ordinary electromagnetic signal.

There are other possible advantages in the use of optical cables. They are generally accepted as being more secure, since it is very difficult to "tap" into this type of cable. The lack of any radiated signal from the cable also helps in this respect. Fibre-optic cables also represent less of a fire hazard. Because they do not carry electric currents, there is no risk of overloads and cables burning out, or sparking that could ignite fumes.

Drawbacks

Although optical cables undoubtedly have advantages, they are not without a few drawbacks as well. At one time they were very costly, and even today this type of cable is far from cheap. Unless you can obtain some suitable cable at low cost from an electronic surplus dealer you will probably have to pay something like one pound per metre for standard 2.2/1 fibre-optic cable. As you are unlikely to be using this cable in large quantities this is not necessarily a major drawback. Also, it has to be borne in mind that an optical cable is normally being used in place of a high quality screened cable. Good quality screened leads are not particularly cheap either, and in some cases are comparable to the cost of an optical cable. Nevertheless, fibre-optics do not usually represent a cheap solution to a problem.

The type of cable you are most likely to use has an inner filament that is one millimetre in diameter, but with the opaque sleeving the overall diameter is 2.2 millimetres (or 2.25 millimetres in some cases). This is quite thin compared to most screened leads, and one might reasonably expect fibre-optic cables to be very flexible. In fact they are usually semi-rigid, and are not easily taken through tight bends. Forming corners with this type of cable is not a practical proposition anyway. Optical cables have a minimum bend radius that is typically about 15 to 50 millimetres, and taking them through a tighter bend is almost certain to damage the inner filament. There is no easy way of cutting out the damaged section of a cable and joining it back together again, so a damaged cable will usually be more or less a write-off.

When using ordinary electric cables the losses through the cable are usually so low that they are of no practical significance. It is only when very long cables are used that the attenuation through the cable becomes a significant factor. High losses through optical cables have been something of a problem in the past, and it is something that remains a significant problem, particularly with low cost cables. For an ordinary fibre-optic cable the loss is typically a little over 1dB per metre, or a loss of about 20% or so per metre in other words. Some modern and reasonably inexpensive cables offer very low losses of about 0.2dB per metre, but only over a very narrow range of wavelengths. The RS/Electromail cable, for example, has a quoted attenuation of 200dB per kilometre at 660 nanometres (the red-orange part of the spectrum), but some 1500dB per kilometre at 820 nanometres (in the "near" infra-red part of the spectrum).

I have mostly experimented with optical cables about 10 to 20 metres long, which provide about 12 to 24dB of attenuation. This means that the intensity of the light fed into the cable has to be about four to sixteen times higher than the required light output level from the cable. Despite these relatively high losses, I have never experienced any real difficulty in getting fibre-optic systems to operate over a range of 20 metres. However, obtaining an operating range of much more than this would probably be quite difficult unless low loss cable is used. Of course, a range of up to about 20 metres is adequate for many practical applications. The communications systems featured in this book will work at ranges of up to about 20 metres with a loss of about 30dB or less through the cable. Using a cable and photocells that provide low losses should permit operation over a distance of more than 100 metres, but I have not tried any of the systems over a range as long as this, and can not guarantee that they will work over such long distances.

I suppose that the most major drawback of fibre-optic cables is simply that they are not directly compatible with normal electrical signals. You can not simply plug one end of an optical cable into the audio output socket of an f.m. tuner, and plug the other end into the audio input of a hi-fi amplifier. There are actually a few pieces of electronic equipment that have built-in optical interfacing, and which can be used with optical cables. Apart from these few exceptions though, using a fibre-optic cable requires some additional circuitry at both ends of the cable. Unfortunately, this extra circuitry normally has to be something more than a photocell at each end of the cable. The additional circuits are not necessarily very complex, but there is always some additional expense, and this over and above any extra cost for the optical cable.

On Reflection

Many people seem to be under the impression that a fibre-optic cable is just a thin filament of glass within an opaque sleeving. In reality things are not quite this simple. These days the

4

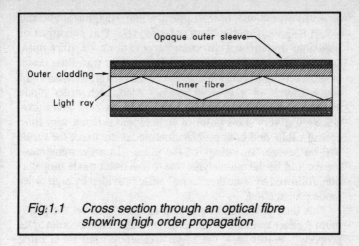

Fig. 1.1   Cross section through an optical fibre
            showing high order propagation

filament is more likely to be polymer (plastic) than glass, and
the cable will have the basic make-up outlined in Figure 1.1.
The filament has a central core which has a high
refractive index, and an outer layer which has a lower refractive index. Reflection where the inner core and the outer layer
meet enables a light ray to travel down the cable by effectively
bouncing from wall to wall. It is this bouncing process that
enables the cable to act as a light guide, since the reflections
will still occur if the cable is taken through a series of curves.
However, it should be noted that taking a cable through a long
and intricate series of bends may reduce the efficiency with
which light is transmitted by the cable. There is a popular joke
in electronic circles about the lady who tied a knot in the mains
cable of an electric iron to hinder the flow of power to the heat-
ing element, and make the iron run cooler. This type of thing
does not work with electric cables, but tying a few knots in a
fibre-optic cable would presumably increase its attenuation
figure quite significantly!

The angle at which the light is reflected along the cable is
dependent on the characteristics of the cable, and the angle at
which the light rays enter the cable. The light in Figure 1.1 is
propagated along the cable in what is termed "high order
mode". Light entering the cable at a lower angle would be

reflected off the wall of the cable at a more shallow angle, and would be propagated in "low order mode". This is not just of academic importance in some applications of fibre-optic cables. The important point here is that light travelling down the cable in high order mode has to travel further than light which travels in low order mode. Also, high order mode involves more reflections for propagation over a given distance. If a very short pulse of light is sent down a very long optical cable, and both propagation modes are used, the result will be severe "smearing" of the pulse. In an extreme case there could be the main signal due to low order mode propagation, followed by a weaker "echo" pulse provided by high order mode propagation.

This dual propagation places a definite limit on the maximum frequency that a given length of cable can accommodate properly. Fortunately, the upper frequency limit for a cable some 20 metres or so in length is far too high for it to be a practical consideration with the circuits provided here. It is a problem that only bothers those at the "leading edge" of fibre-optic technology. So-called "single mode" cables which only support one or other of the propagation modes are produced, but they have no advantage when used with the projects described in this book. Any fibre-optic cable of reasonable quality should be perfectly suitable.

There is an alternative form of optical cable which is called a "graded index" cable. A normal optical cable is a "stepped index" type incidentally. The two types of cable are very similar in construction and the way they operate, but the graded index type has a gradual transition from high reflective index central core to a lower index outer layer. This results in the light still travelling down the cable in much the same way as for a stepped index cable, but with the light taking a curved route, as in Figure 1.2. Stepped index and graduated index cables are both suitable for the projects featured in this book.

The standard size for optical cables is an overall diameter of 2.2 millimetres (or 2.25 millimetres) and a filament diameter of 1 millimetre. A cable of this type is easy to use with the special fibre optic LEDs and phototransistors that are available to amateur users. You may find other sizes of optical cable listed in one or two component catalogues, and various types seem

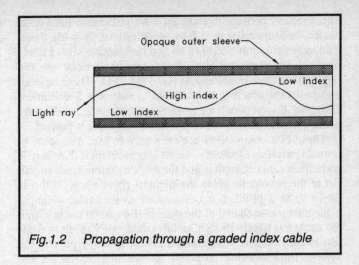

Fig.1.2   *Propagation through a graded index cable*

to be offered by electronic surplus dealers from time to time. These alternative cables include types which have a very fine filament, and multi-core cables. It might be possible to use other types and sizes of optical cable with the circuits featured in this book, but the only way to find out is to try it and see.

Probably in most cases it would be possible, but a little ingenuity might be needed in order to connect the cable to the photocells successfully. However, I would advise against the use of cables having very fine filaments. I have found it virtually impossible to obtain good results using this type of cable with ordinary fibre-optic photocells. The problem seems to be that the very fine filament provides a light output at a high enough intensity, but over too small an area. This gives too little light to drive the relatively large area of a normal phototransistor or photodiode. There is also a slight problem with multi-cored cables, which can be relatively expensive even when purchased from a surplus dealer.

Photocells
When choosing the photocells for use with fibre-optic cables there are three basic choices. The obvious one is to use the special fibre-optic LEDs and phototransistors that are available.

These readily connect to standard 2.2/1 millimetre fibre-optic cables, and are guaranteed to work efficiently with them. Currently there only seems to be two inexpensive sets of fibre-optic photocells available. The cheapest devices are the SFH350 phototransistor and SFH750 red LED. These have an encapsulation which is very similar to that of a 5 millimetre LED, but it is somewhat elongated, and has a 2.2 millimetre diameter aperture into which the end of the cable is pushed.

These two components are very easy to use, and seem to provide excellent efficiency. One slight problem is that there is no built-in cable clamping, and the cable therefore tends to pull out of the photocells given the slightest opportunity. If this is likely to be a problem it is necessary to improvise a simple cable clamp at each end of the system. Be careful not to clamp the cable too tightly though, as this could easily result in damage to the filament, which would almost certainly prevent the system from working properly. Connection details for the SFH350 and SFH750 are provided in Figure 1.3.

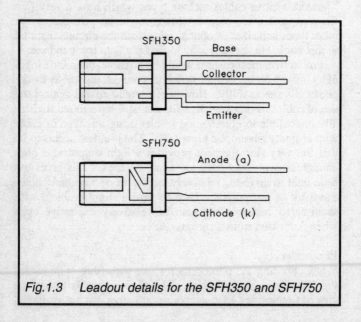

Fig.1.3   Leadout details for the SFH350 and SFH750

The alternative photocells are the MFOE71 and MFOE76 LEDs, and the MFOD71 photodiode. The difference between the two LEDs is that the MFOE71 is an infra-red type whereas the MFOE76 is a visible red LED. Most fibre-optic cables work well with visible light and the so-called "near" infra-red wavelengths (which is the part of the infra-red spectrum in which infra-red LEDs operate). The MFOD71 detector also works well over this range. Results should therefore be much the same regardless of which LED is used. The exception is when using a cable that has a response which peaks strongly at light wavelength of around 660 nanometres. With this type of cable it would obviously be better to use the MFOE76 which has maximum output at 660 nanometres. Incidentally, the SFH750 will also work very efficiently with this type of cable.

The MFO*** photocells are somewhat more expensive than the SFH350/750, but they are mechanically somewhat more complex. They are designed for printed circuit mounting, and have provision for an 8BA fixing bolt so that they can be firmly fixed to the board. They also have a sort of built-in screw terminal that enables the fibre-optic cable to be securely held in

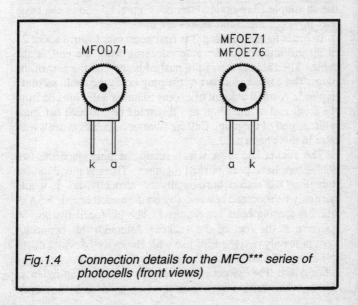

Fig.1.4   Connection details for the MFO*** series of
photocells (front views)

place. This is a definite improvement on the simple push-fit of the SFH350 and SFH750, but it requires a few millimetres of the outer sleeving to be removed from each end of the cable. It can be a bit tricky to do this without doing serious damage to the cable. Figure 1.4 provides connection details for the MFO*** series of devices. These show the devices viewed from the front (i.e. looking at the aperture into which the cable fits).

Fibre-Optic Connectors

The main alternative to using special fibre-optic photocells is to use ordinary LEDs, phototransistors, and photodiodes, but in conjunction with the fibre-optic connectors that are available. These connectors are the fibre-optic equivalents of ordinary electrical plugs and sockets. Quite a wide range of fibre-optic connectors are manufactured, but most of these are relatively expensive and a bit "over the top" for our requirements. The RS/Electromail "dnp" (dry non-polish) connectors are probably the best choice for the home constructor. These are very easy to use, inexpensive, and are perfectly adequate for use in simple fibre-optic systems. Figure 1.5 shows the basic way in which these connectors are used.

In order to use the plug it is first necessary to strip about 25 to 30 millimetres of the outer sleeving from the end of the cable. The cable is then fully pushed home into the rear of the plug. The barbed rear part of the plug holds the cable securely in place. A small amount of excess filament will protrude from the front end of the plug, and this must be trimmed off flush with the end of the plug. Cutting fibre-optic cables is dealt with later in this chapter.

The socket has arms which retain the plug once the two connectors have been pushed together. There is provision for mounting the socket horizontally or vertically, but it would normally be mounted horizontally on the circuit board. 8BA or M2.5 mounting bolts are required. The photocell fits into an aperture at the rear of the socket. Although this connector system is only designed for use with Honeywell devices of the "sweet spot" variety, it will work reasonably well using many other types. The "sweet spot" components have built-in lenses which make them very efficient when used with fibre-optic

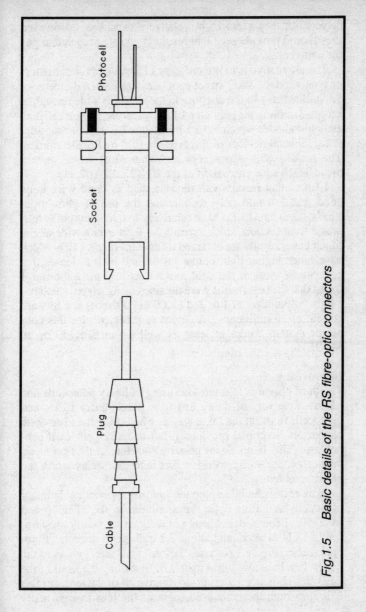

Fig.1.5   Basic details of the RS fibre-optic connectors

cables, but they seem to be relatively expensive. However, they should provide excellent results if you are prepared to pay the extra cost.

The alternative is to use ordinary LEDs and phototransistors or photodiodes. The "sweet spot" devices have a diameter of 5.6 millimetres, so the aperture in the socket is wide enough to accept 5 millimetre diameter LEDs, plus the phototransistors and photodiodes which have 5 millimetre LED-like encapsulations. Several devices of this type are sold by RS/Electromail. The sockets will also accept phototransistors which have a metal TO18 style case, such as the BPX25, BPY62, etc.

I found that results with devices such as these were quite good, but I would only recommend the use of ultra-bright LEDs. Ordinary LEDs have relatively low light output levels, plus a front section which spreads the light over a wide angle. Much better results are obtained using ultra-bright LEDs which have much higher light output levels, and built-in lenses that concentrate most of the light into a relatively narrow beam. I found that the best results were obtained using a type which has a light output level of 1 or 2cd (1000 to 2000mcd) at a forward current of 20 milliamps. A device of this type plus this connector system works at least as well as an SFH750 or an MFOE76.

Improvising

The third option is to improvise using ordinary photocells and LEDs. One way of doing this is to use ordinary LEDs and photocells in much the same way as when using the fibre-optic connectors described previously, but to make your own connectors. This is no doubt possible, but the "real" fibre-optic connectors are so inexpensive that it hardly seems worth the effort involved.

A more worthwhile approach is to try converting ordinary photocells into fibre-optic types, similar to the SFH350 and SFH750. I found that it was not difficult to modify an ultra-bright LED to accommodate a 2.2 millimetre diameter fibre-optic cable. Figure 1.6 shows "before" and "after" views of the LED. It is basically just a matter of first filing the front of the LED flat. It is not necessary to remove all of the lens. In fact it is important to remove no more of the lens than is really

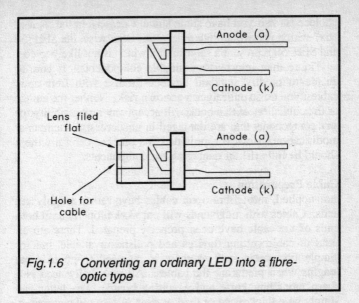

Fig.1.6 Converting an ordinary LED into a fibre-optic type

necessary. You simply need to produce a flat surface so that a hole having a diameter of 2.2 millimetres can be drilled into the front of the component. I found that the best way of making the hole was to grip the cell horizontally in the grooved jaws of a "Workmate", and to then carefully drill the hole using a small hand-drill. The hole must be drilled fairly deeply so that the end of the cable is brought close to the "business" part of the component, but care must be taken not to drill so deeply that the internal structure of the component is damaged.

I found that improvised fibre-optic components worked surprisingly well. In fact an ultra-bright LED modified in this way coupled much more light into the cable than most "proper" fibre-optic LEDs. In fact high output types having outputs of about 100 to 250mcd seem to be perfectly adequate, but ordinary "bog standard" LEDs are unlikely to give good results. Reasonable results are obtained using a modified phototransistor of the type which has a 5 millimetre LED type encapsulation.

It is probably only worthwhile trying this method if you experience difficulty in obtaining "real" fibre-optic LEDs and photocells, or if you have some suitable devices in the "spares box" which you would like to try out. Otherwise, the SFH350 and SFH750 represent a safer option which is not likely to cost any more than improvising suitable components. If you do decide to modify standard devices for use with fibre-optic cables, you do so entirely at your own risk. Neither the author or the publishers of this book will accept any responsibility for any components that are damaged in unsuccessful attempts at modification. However, provided you proceed carefully there should be little risk of damaging the components.

Cable Preparation

As supplied, most fibre-optic cables have rather roughly cut ends. Cables with rough ends will not work properly until both ends of the cable have been properly prepared. There are all sorts of cable cutting devices and polishes available, but for simple fibre-optic systems there is no need to go to great lengths when preparing the cables. All you really need is a sharp modelling knife and a cutting board. The latter can simply be a thick piece of card or even just an old newspaper. All you have to do is cut cleanly through the cable in one go using plenty of pressure. Make the cut a few millimetres from the end of the cable so that there is minimal wastage, and be sure that the cut is reasonably perpendicular to the cable. The end of the filament should have a smooth shiny surface, and the cable should work efficiently without the need for any polishing. Obviously both ends of the cable must be prepared in this way, and due care should be taken to avoid cutting yourself or the worktop.

Some fibre-optic devices and connector systems require a small piece of sleeving to be removed from each end of the cable. Special strippers are available, but are rather expensive if they will only receive occasional use. Some ordinary wire strippers work well with many fibre-optic cables. It is therefore worth trying your wire strippers to see how well (or otherwise) they perform with the particular optical cable you are using. If they damage the filament there is no major harm done, since you can cut off the damaged end of the cable and try again using another method. No more than a few millimetres of cable will have been wasted.

Probably the best approach if your wire strippers will not do the job is to use a sharp modelling knife. Make a lengthwise cut in the sleeving at the end of the cable. Try to cut reasonably deeply, but if possible avoid cutting into the polymer filament. It should then be possible to peel back the sleeving over the full length of the cut. The peeled-back section of sleeving is easily cut away using the modelling knife or a small but sharp pair of scissors. If might take one or two attempts to get it just right, but even if there should be a slight score mark in the exposed filament, it is unlikely that this will greatly reduce the efficiency of the cable. On the other hand, a deep cut into the filament will almost certainly prevent the cable from giving satisfactory results.

The MFOE71, MFOE76, and MFOD71, plus 1/2.2 fibre-optic cable are available from:

Maplin Electronics Ltd.,

P.O. Box 3,

Rayleigh,

Essex,

SS6 2BR.

(Tel. 01702 552911)

The SFH350 and SFH750 are available from:

Electrovalue Ltd.,

Unit 3,

Central Trading Estate,

Staines,

TW18 4UX.

(Tel. 01784 442253)

The fibre-optic connectors, "sweet spot" photocells, and 1/2.2 fibre-optic cable are available from:

Electromail,

P.O. Box 33,

Corby,

Northants.,

NN17 9EL,

(Tel. 01536 204555)

Chapter 2

ANALOGUE LINKS

On the face of it, there is little difficulty in using a fibre-optic link to carry analogue signals. It is just a matter of using the input signal at the transmitter to vary the brightness of the LED, and a photocell plus load resistor at the receiver to convert the changing light level back to a varying voltage. In reality such a system will work, but not particularly well. There is a minor problem in that the output voltage from the receiver is likely to be far lower than the input voltage swing to the transmitter. This attenuation occurs due to various losses in the system, but is easily balanced by some amplification at the receiver. The main problem is a lack of linearity. This is in turn due to a lack of good linearity in the LED and the photocell.

A.M. Link

There is no easy way of counteracting the inherent non-linearity of the system, and it is something that just has to be tolerated if a basic a.m. (amplitude modulation) system is used. The quality obtained is fine for something as basic as a voice link, and is usually just about acceptable for a mid-fi music link, but a simple a.m. link is unsuitable for anything beyond undemanding applications such as these.

The circuit diagram for a simple a.m. fibre-optic link is shown in Figure 2.1 (transmitter) and Figure 2.2 (receiver). The transmitter circuit is very simple, and it is basically just an operational amplifier used in the non-inverting mode, and having a discrete emitter follower output stage which drives the fibre-optic LED (D1). R3 and R4 set the closed loop voltage gain of the amplifier at just under 6 times, which means that about 350 millivolts r.m.s. is needed at the input in order to fully drive the transmitter. If necessary, the sensitivity can be boosted somewhat by making R3 higher in value.

R5 is the current limiting resistor for D1, and this sets the quiescent LED current at about 4 milliamps or so. When the circuit is fully modulated the LED current therefore varies between about 0 and 9 milliamps, but the average LED current

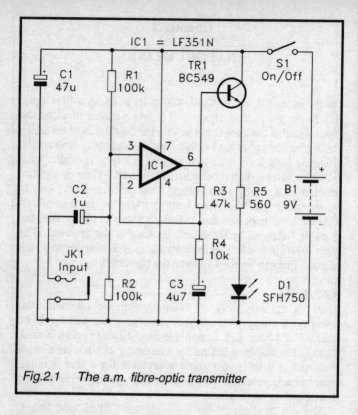

Fig.2.1   The a.m. fibre-optic transmitter

remains more or less unchanged at around 4.5 milliamps. The system should work quite well with this fairly modest LED current, but a higher current can be used if the output from the transmitter is found to be rather weak. A value of about 270R will give a LED current of about 10 milliamps, or a value of 120R will produce a LED current of approximately 20 milliamps. It should definitely not be necessary to use a current of more than 20 milliamps. There is a fault somewhere in the system if a LED current as high as 20 milliamps fails to give good results. The current consumption of the circuit as a whole is about 1 milliamp more than the LED current, or about 5.5 milliamps using the specified values.

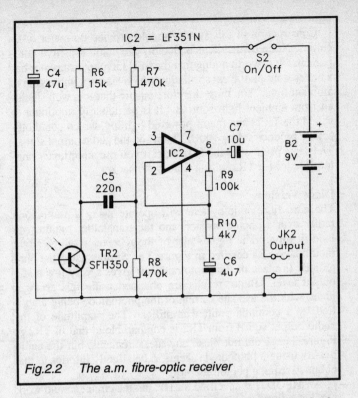

Fig.2.2   The a.m. fibre-optic receiver

The receiver circuit is equally straightforward. TR2 is the phototransistor, and R6 is its load resistor. In darkness the leakage current through TR2 is very low, and is likely to be well under one microamp. The light from the transmitter produces an increase in the leakage level, and the higher the light level, the greater the leakage current. This varying leakage current produces a varying voltage at the collector of TR2, and the voltage change here is roughly proportional to the change in input voltage to the transmitter. The output signal from TR2 is relatively weak though, and IC2 is therefore used to boost the signal to a level that is comparable to the input level at the transmitter. IC2 operates as a non-inverting amplifier having a closed loop voltage gain of approximately 22 times. The current consumption of the receiver circuit is only about 1.5

milliamps.

Construction of this system should provide no major difficulties. None of the semiconductors are static sensitive components. It is worth noting that the SFH350 phototransistor has a transparent plastic encapsulation which leaves it vulnerable to ambient light. You must therefore ensure that it is well shielded from ambient light sources. It is particularly important to shield the TR2 from mains powered lighting, which could otherwise produce strong 100Hz "hum" on the audio output signal. The same problem is likely to exist if you use an ordinary phototransistor for TR2, plus a fibre-optic socket.

Diode Versions

The a.m. fibre-optic system will operate using a photodiode rather than a phototransistor, and the transmitter requires no modification. The input stage of the receiver requires slight modification, as detailed in Figure 2.3. Simply using the photodiode in place of the phototransistor gives a very low audio output level. Better results are obtained using this arrangement, with the leakage current of the photodiode being amplified by a common emitter amplifier. The amplitude of the audio output signal from TR2 is comparable to that of TR2 in Figure 2.2. I did not make any measurements, but the audio quality using a photodiode seems to be slightly inferior to that obtained using a phototransistor.

An MFOD71 is specified for D2, but the circuit should work much the same using any other photodiode that can provide a similar degree of sensitivity. When using the MFOD71 in the receiver the MFOE71 or MFOE76 LED would presumably be used in the D1 position at the transmitter (but an SFH750 seems to work perfectly well with the MFOD71). Note that about 2.5 to 5 millimetres of sleeving must be removed from each end of the cable before it will connect to any of the MFO*** devices properly. Make sure that the cable is fully pushed into the photocell before tightening its locking nut. The cable is not pushed in far enough if tightening the nut does not secure the cable in place.

Two way communications using ordinary electric cables is easy enough, and it simply requires some switching to connect each end of the cable to a transmitter or receiver circuit, as

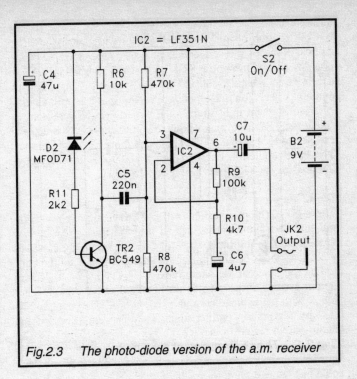

Fig.2.3   The photo-diode version of the a.m. receiver

required. On the face of it there is no easy way of providing
two way communications using a single fibre-optic cable. The
normal solution is to use two cables – one cable for communications in each direction. Twin fibre-optic cable is available
from RS/Electromail. Using a single cable would be a practical proposition if it was possible to use the photocell as both an
emitter and a receiver. This would be the fibre-optic equivalent
of a low cost intercom where the loudspeaker also operates as
a sort of crude moving coil microphone. One of the lesser
known properties of LEDs is that they can actually be used in
reverse as photodiodes, but they do not necessarily operate very
efficiently when used in this way. Nevertheless, by using a
LED in this manner it should be possible to obtain two way
communications using a single fibre-optic cable.

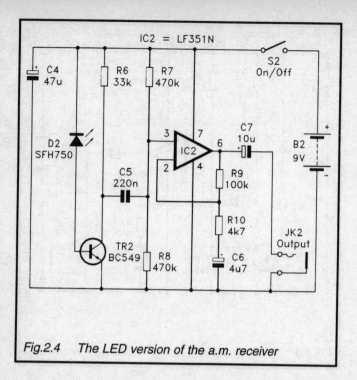

Fig.2.4   The LED version of the a.m. receiver

I managed to obtain reasonable results from the receiver circuit using an SFH750 LED as a photodiode (Figure 2.4). The only problem seems to be a slight lack in sensitivity. The circuit is basically the same as the one used with a "proper" photodiode, but in order to compensate for the lower sensitivity of D2 the value of R6 has been increased. Also, no current limiting resistor has been used in series with D2. Therefore, be very careful to fit D2 with the correct polarity, as an error here will almost certainly "zap" both D2 and TR2.

Despite the modifications this circuit still provides slightly less output than the version which uses a true photodiode for D2. However, the sensitivity of the receiver is still perfectly adequate, and it works rather better than I had expected. I did not try it, but with the aid of a d.p.d.t. switch it would be possible to use the same diode in both the transmitter and receiver circuits, and thereby obtain two way communications over a single fibre-optic cable. Of course, communications would be restricted to one way operation at any one time.

Components for A.M. Fibre Optic System (Figs. 2.1 and 2.2)

Resistors (all 0.25 watt 5% carbon film)
R1	100k
R2	100k
R3	47k
R4	10k
R5	560R
R6	15k
R7	470k
R8	470k
R9	100k
R10	4k7

Capacitors
C1	47µ 16V elect
C2	1µ 50V elect
C3	4µ7 50V elect
C4	47µ 16V elect
C5	220n polyester
C6	4µ7 50V elect
C7	10µ 25V

Semiconductors
IC1	LF351N
IC2	LF351N
TR1	BC549
TR2	SFH350
D1	SFH750

Miscellaneous
S1	s.p.s.t. min toggle
S2	s.p.s.t. min toggle
JK1	3.5mm jack socket
JK2	3.5mm jack socket
B1	9 volt (6 × HP7 size cells in holder)

B2   9 volt (PP3 size)

Cases, circuit boards, PP3 type battery connector (2 off), 8 pin DIL IC holder (2 off), fibre-optic cable, wire, solder, etc.

Altered values and additional components

(Fig. 2.3)

R6	10k
R11	2k2
D2	MFOD71
TR2	BC549

(Fig. 2.4)

R6	33k
D2	SFH750
TR2	BC549

Improved A.M. System

It is possible to compensate for a lack of linearity through an a.m. fibre-optic link by using non-linear negative feedback. In effect, non-linear feedback is used to generate distortion that is equal and opposite to the distortion through the link. The "anti-distortion" balances out the distortion in the system to give perfect linearity. In practice it is not usually possible to achieve a very high degree of linearity due to problems in generating "anti-distortion" that precisely cancels the normal distortion of the system. It is possible to obtain much improved results though.

This method of improving linearity is sometimes used when coupling a signal through an opto-isolator. Figure 2.5 shows the basic arrangement used. TR1 and D1 are an opto-isolator which is used in the negative feedback path, while D2 and TR2 form the opto-isolator that is used to provide the coupling. Of course, in practice the input and output circuits of this second opto-isolator would be operated from separate supplies, but this is irrelevant to the basic functioning of the link. The circuit is based on a high gain amplifier, which in practice is normally an operational amplifier.

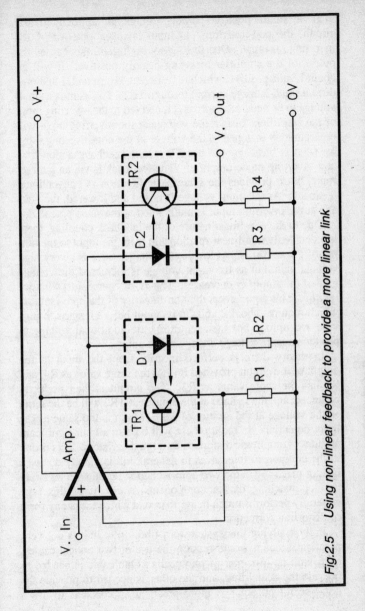

Fig.2.5   Using non-linear feedback to provide a more linear link

If a small positive input voltage is applied to the circuit, the non-inverting (+) input is taken positive of the inverting (-) input. Due to its very high gain, this causes the output of the amplifier to swing heavily positive. It will go about 2 volts positive, which is sufficient to turn on D1 and produce a small leakage current through TR1. This causes a small voltage to be generated across R1, and fed to the inverting input of the amplifier. In fact the voltage at the inverting input will be accurately matched to the voltage at the non-inverting input by what is basically the usual negative feedback action of a non-inverting mode amplifier. The feedback is via an indirect route, but it provides the same basic function as conventional feedback. As the input voltage is raised and lowered, the voltage at the inverting input is maintained at the same potential.

Due to the non-linear nature of the feedback coupling, there is a decidedly non-linear relationship from the input to the output of the amplifier. At low input voltages there is a very high voltage gain, but as the input voltage is increased the voltage gain of the amplifier decreases. This is, of course, just what we require. This counteracts the non-linearity of the opto-isolator, which requires about 2 volts at its input before it starts to provide a coupling, but then requires little additional voltage to produce a large voltage change at the output.

In theory there is perfect linearity from the input to the output of the circuit provided R1 has the same value as R4, and R2 has the same value as R3. The circuit is then perfectly balanced, and the voltage at the emitter of TR2 will be the same as the voltage at the emitter of TR1 (which is the same as the input potential). In reality there will be a small but significant amount of amplitude distortion through the system. This is due to the component tolerances in general, but is mainly due to a lack of matching in the two opto-isolators. Even with less than perfect matching of the components, a circuit of this type generally performs much better than one which lacks any form of distortion correction.

Fully applying this system to a fibre-optic link is not very practical, since it would require the use of two optical cables, each with its own pair of photocells. One cable is needed to provide the actual link, and the other is needed to provide the non-linear feedback. A more practical approach is to use a

26

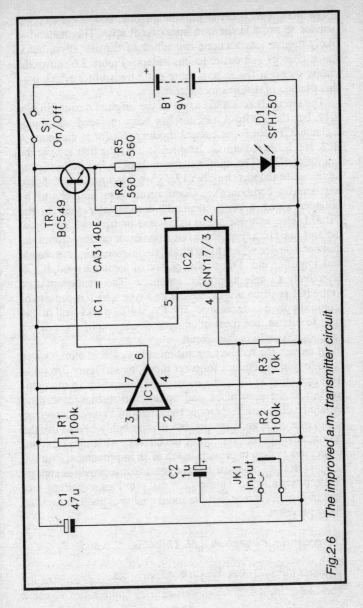

Fig.2.6   The improved a.m. transmitter circuit

single fibre-optic cable to provide the link, and to use an opto-isolator to provide the non-linear feedback. This method is likely to give less accurate cancelling of the distortion, but is much cheaper and easier to implement. Figure 2.6 shows the circuit diagram for an a.m. fibre-optic transmitter which uses this method of distortion cancelling.

The circuit is much the same as the original design (Figure 2.1), but the feedback resistor has been replaced with opto-isolator IC2. R4 is the current limiting resistor at the input of IC2, and R3 is the emitter load resistor for the transistor at the output of IC2. The opto-isolator must be a fast and efficient device. I found that the CNY17/3 gave good results, as should any similar component. Good results are unlikely to be obtained using a "bog standard" opto-isolator such as the TIL111, etc., as these are too slow and inefficient. The opto-isolator must be a type which has a transistor on the output side, and not a device which has a diode, darlington pair, photodiode and amplifier, etc. Due to the method of feedback used, IC1 is effectively a single supply d.c. amplifier. The component used in the IC1 position must therefore be a type which is capable of single supply d.c. operation. The CA3140E works well in this type of circuit, but most other operational amplifiers will not function properly in this circuit.

In theory, the receiver circuit must have the phototransistor operating in the emitter follower mode, as in Figure 2.7. It is then operating in the same mode as the transistor in the opto-isolator at the transmitter, and optimum distortion cancelling should be obtained. In practice the circuit of Figure 2.2 seemed to provide quite good results, but it is probably best to use the "politically correct" version of the circuit. Although I did not expect this system to provide much of an improvement over the original design, practical tests suggest that it provides significantly better results. This system still provides something less than hi-fi performance, but the audio quality is good enough for many purposes.

Components for Improved A.M. Link (Figs. 2.6 and 2.7)

Resistors (all 0.25 watt 5% carbon film)
R1   100k

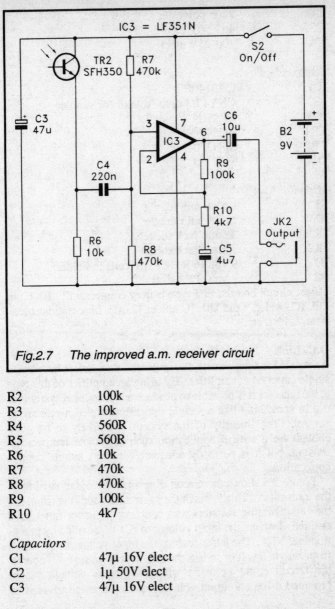

Fig.2.7   The improved a.m. receiver circuit

R2	100k
R3	10k
R4	560R
R5	560R
R6	10k
R7	470k
R8	470k
R9	100k
R10	4k7

Capacitors
C1	47µ 16V elect
C2	1µ 50V elect
C3	47µ 16V elect

29

C4	220n polyester
C5	4μ7 50V elect
C6	10μ 25V elect

Semiconductors

IC1	CA3140E
IC2	CNY17/3 opto-isolator (or similar)
IC3	LF351N
TR1	BC549
TR2	SFH350
D1	SFH750

Miscellaneous

S1	s.p.s.t. min toggle
S2	s.p.s.t. min toggle
JK1	3.5mm jack socket
JK2	3.5mm jack socket
B1	9 volt (6 × HP7 size cells in holder)
B2	9 volt (PP3 size)

Cases, circuit boards, PP3 type battery connector (2 off), 6 pin DIL IC holder, 8 pin DIL IC holder (2 off), fibre-optic cable, wire, solder, etc.

D.C. Link

As pointed out previously, the improved a.m. link is based on a single supply d.c. amplifier. By using an amplifier of this type at the receiver it is possible to produce a d.c. coupled system for use in something like a simple optically coupled motor speed control. The linearity of the system is unlikely to be good enough for a critical application such as remote temperature sensing, but it is perfectly adequate for most simple control applications.

Figure 2.8 shows the circuit diagram for the d.c. version of the transmitter. This is much the same as the audio version, but the input biasing resistors and coupling capacitor have been omitted. Instead, the input voltage to IC1 is provided by potentiometer VR1. The latter enables the input voltage to be varied from zero to a volt or so less than the supply voltage. Of course, the circuit could be used with a different voltage source provided it has an output voltage within the range covered by

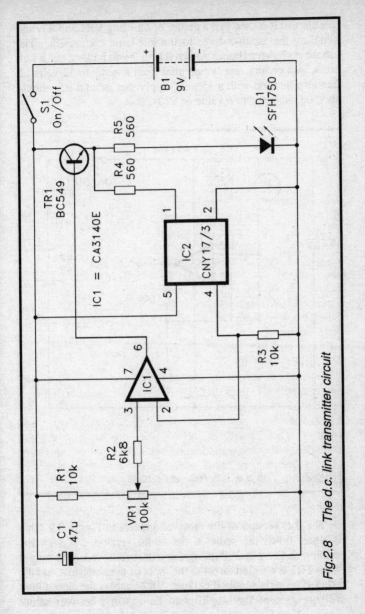

Fig.2.8   The d.c. link transmitter circuit

31

this circuit. It is then just a matter of omitting VR1 and R1, and coupling the input voltage to the left hand end of R2. The circuit is shown as being powered by a 9 volt battery, but it will work well on any supply potential from about 9 to 12 volts. It can also be used with a 15 volt supply, but R4 and R5 should then be increased to a value of 820 ohms.

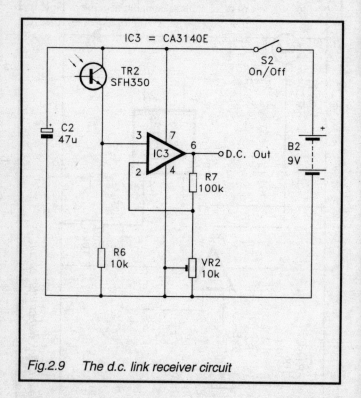

Fig.2.9   The d.c. link receiver circuit

The d.c. version of the receiver appears in Figure 2.9. This is again much the same as the audio version, but with the biasing resistors and coupling capacitors removed. The output from TR2 is coupled direct to the input of the amplifier, and the latter is a single supply d.c. type. VR2 enables the closed loop voltage gain of the amplifier to be adjusted between about eleven times and the full open loop gain of IC3. This component is adjusted so that maximum output voltage from IC3 is just about achieved when VR1 at the transmitter is set for maximum wiper voltage. If a very short optical cable is used it might be necessary to reduce the value of R7 in order to achieve this. The output of IC3 should then track changes in the wiper voltage of VR1 with reasonable accuracy. Note that the maximum output voltage is a volt or two less than the supply voltage. The circuit will work well using any supply voltage from around 9 to 18 volts.

Components for D.C. Link (Figs. 2.8 and 2.9)

Resistors (all 0.25 watt 5% carbon film)

R1	10k
R2	6k8
R3	10k
R4	560R
R5	560R
R6	10k
R7	100k

Potentiometers

VR1	100k lin carbon
VR2	10k min preset

Capacitors

C1	47µ 16V elect
C2	47µ 25V elect

Semiconductors

IC1	CA3140E
IC2	CNY17/3 opto-isolator (or similar)
IC3	CA3140E
D1	SFH750
TR1	BC549
TR2	SFH350

Miscellaneous

S1	s.p.s.t. min toggle

S2	min toggle
B1	9 volt (6 × HP7 size cells in holder)
B2	9 volt (PP3 size)

Cases, circuit boards, PP3 type battery connector (2 off), 6 pin DIL IC holder, 8 pin DIL IC holder (2 off), control knob, fibre-optic cable, wire, solder, etc.

F.M. Audio Link

The non-linearity through the photocells of a fibre-optic audio link does not necessarily have to result in distortion through the system. Using some form of digital system it is possible to render the non-linearity of the basic link of no practical importance. The optical link only has to couple logic signals, with their two stable levels (logic 0 or "low", and logic 1 or "high"). Even very severe amplitude distortion is irrelevant when coupling logic signals. This does not mean that coupling an audio signal through a fibre-optic link in digital form will provide zero distortion. What it does mean is that the distortion is determined by other factors, and mainly by linearity of the modulator and demodulator, rather than by the optical link. Provided a good quality modulator and demodulator are used, the distortion levels should be very low.

There are two basic methods of coupling an audio signal through a fibre-optic cable in digital form. These are to use frequency modulation (f.m.) and pulse width modulation (p.w.m.). Systems using both methods will be covered here, starting with an f.m. audio link. In essence a system of this type operates in the same way as a radio receiver tuned to a v.h.f. band II transmission. In this case the carrier frequency is much lower though. In fact it is about one thousand times lower (about 100kHz instead of 100MHz).

Figure 2.10 shows the block diagram for the f.m. audio link. The VCO (voltage controlled oscillator) is at the heart of the transmitter section of the unit. This feeds the infra-red LED via a buffer stage that enables the LED to be driven at a suitably high current. The control input of the VCO is driven from the audio input socket via a buffer amplifier and a lowpass filter. The lowpass filter removes input signals at high frequencies which could otherwise react with the VCO signal

34

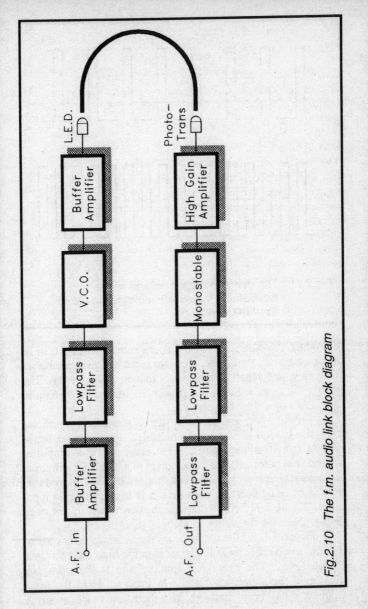

Fig.2.10 The f.m. audio link block diagram

35

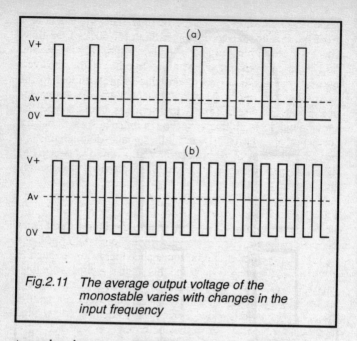

Fig.2.11 The average output voltage of the monostable varies with changes in the input frequency

to produce beat notes. The VCO operates at about 80kHz or so under quiescent conditions. Positive input half cycles raise its frequency, and negative half cycles reduce its frequency. The greater the input voltage, the greater the increase/reduction in the VCO's operating frequency.

At the receiving end of the system a photodiode or phototransistor is used to convert the pulses of light from the transmitter to small voltage pulses. A two stage high gain amplifier is needed in order to boost these pulses to a level that will drive the next stage properly. This is a monostable, and it produces a pulse of fixed duration each time it is triggered by an input pulse. Figure 2.11 helps to explain the way in which this stage demodulates the frequency modulated input signal.

In Figure 2.11(a) the output from the monostable has a 1 to 3 mark-space ratio, and the output is in the high state for 25% of the time. The average output voltage is therefore one quarter of the supply potential. In Figure 2.11(b) the input frequency has been doubled, and there are twice as many output pulses in a given period of time. This gives a 1 to 1 mark-space ratio, and the output is high for 50% of the time. The average output voltage is half the supply voltage, and double the previous output potential. In other words, the average output voltage of the monostable is proportional to the input frequency, and the required frequency-to-voltage conversion is being provided. The output signal is a pulsed type, but a lowpass filter is all that is needed in order to smooth out the pulses and recover the original audio signal. Although this is a very simple form of demodulator, with a low frequency FM signal it actually works quite well, and provides surprisingly good linearity.

The Circuits

The circuit diagram for the f.m. transmitter appears in Figure 2.12. IC1 is a buffer stage which provides an input impedance of 50k. It provides an output impedance that is low enough to drive the next stage properly, and this stage is a third order lowpass filter based on IC2. The cutoff frequency of this filter is approximately 20kHz. Therefore, this filter does not restrict the audio bandwidth of the unit. It only attenuates unwanted signals at frequencies above the audio range.

The output of IC2 is coupled to the control input of the VCO. The latter uses the oscillator section of IC3, which is a CMOS 4046BE "micro-power" phase locked loop. In this circuit only the VCO section of this device is utilized, and no connections are made to the phase comparators, etc. R6 and R7 provide a bias voltage of just under half the supply voltage to IC3's control input. C7 and R8 are the timing components, and they give a centre frequency of approximately 80kHz. A good quality squarewave output signal is produced at pin 4 of IC3, and this drives the fibre-optic LED (D1) via an emitter follower buffer amplifier (TR1). R9 sets the "on" LED current at about 32 milliamps, which gives an average LED current of around 16 milliamps.

The receiver circuit diagram is shown in Figures 2.13 and 2.14. Figure 2.13 shows the circuit for the amplifier and monostable stages. The photocell is a photodiode, and it is its varying reverse bias leakage that produces an output signal from the received light pulses. R10 is the load resistor for D2.

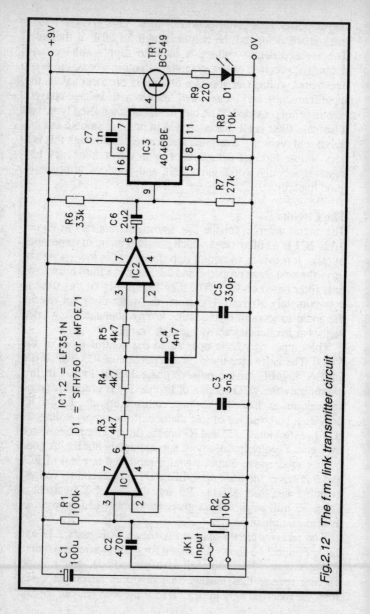

Fig.2.12 The f.m. link transmitter circuit

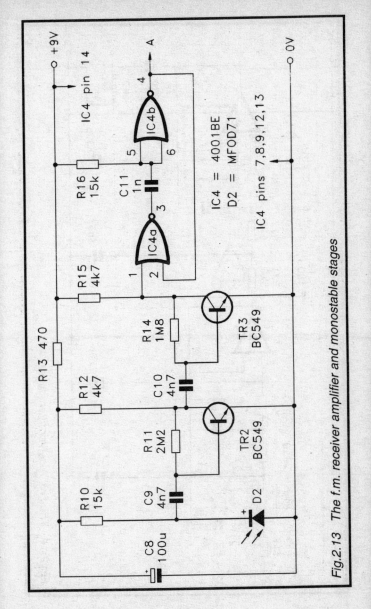

Fig.2.13 The f.m. receiver amplifier and monostable stages

39

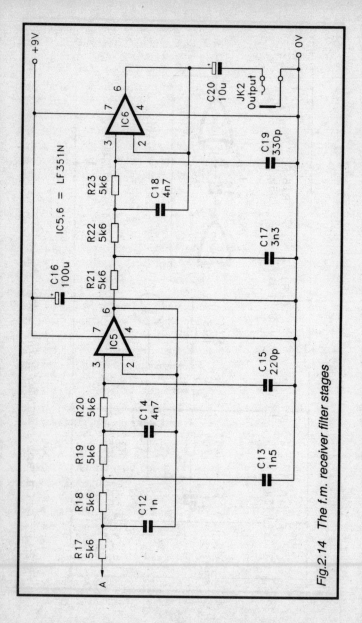

Fig.2.14 The f.m. receiver filter stages

The amplifier consists of two common emitter amplifiers which have a combined voltage gain of over 80dB. These provide good results even if a long cable is used, and the light output signal received by TR2 is quite weak.

The monostable is formed from two of the NOR gates in IC4, which is a CMOS quad 2 input NOR gate package. The other two gates are left unused, but their inputs are connected to the 0 volt supply rail in order to prevent spurious operation and possible damage by stray static charges. C11 and R16 are the timing components, and these set the pulse duration at approximately 9μs. This is comfortably shorter than the duration of one input cycle from the transmitter, but is long enough to give a strong output signal from the system.

Figure 2.14 shows the circuit diagram for the filter stages. This really consists of two lowpass filters wired in series. IC5 is used as the basis of a fourth order (24dB per octave) filter, and IC6 is used in a third order (18dB per octave type). Both have a cutoff frequency at about 20kHz. Consequently, they do not significantly attenuate audio frequency signals. They do provide a great deal of attenuation at the carrier frequency, and with a combined attenuation rate of 42dB per octave, they provide over 80dB of carrier attenuation. This is sufficient to reduce the carrier breakthrough at the output to under one millivolt peak-to-peak. In some applications it is not necessary to have such a high degree of carrier suppression, and it is then acceptable to omit IC6, C17, C18, C19, and R21 to R23. The positive terminal of C20 then connects to the output (pin 6) of IC5. This leaves four stage filtering, which gives about 48dB of carrier attenuation.

If preferred, a phototransistor can be used as the sensor in the receiver circuit using the modified input circuit of Figure 2.15. The value of load resistor R10 has been reduced somewhat in order to tame the sensitivity of the circuit. This version of the receiver is still likely to be substantially more sensitive than the version which uses a photodiode. However, the noise level from the sensor is significantly higher as well, and the performance of the two circuits for a given input signal strength is not substantially different. If the base terminal of TR4 is accessible (as it is with the SFH350) it is advisable to connect it to the 0 volt supply rail. Otherwise there is a slight risk of

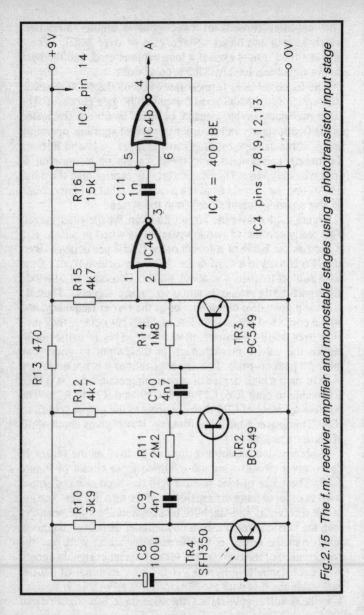

Fig.2.15 The f.m. receiver amplifier and monostable stages using a phototransistor input stage

stray pick up at this terminal producing instability or interference on the output signal.

Construction of these circuits is reasonably straightforward, but the 4046BE is a CMOS device, and the normal anti-static handling precautions should therefore be observed when dealing with this component. If these circuits are powered from a mains power supply unit it must be a type that has a low output noise level.

Components for F.M. Audio Link
(Figs. 2.12, 2.13 and 2.14)

Resistors (all 0.25 watt 5% carbon film)

R1	100k
R2	100k
R3	4k7
R4	4k7
R5	4k7
R6	33k
R7	27k
R8	10k
R9	220R
R10	15k
R11	2M2
R12	4k7
R13	470R
R14	1M8
R15	4k7
R16	15k
R17 to R23	5k6 (7 off)

Capacitors

C1	100µ 10V elect
C2	470n polyester
C3	3n3 polyester
C4	4n7 polyester
C5	330p polystyrene
C6	2µ2 50V elect
C7	1n polyester
C8	100µ 10V elect

C9	4n7 polyester
C10	4n7 polyester
C11	1n polyester
C12	1n polyester
C13	1n5 polyester
C14	4n7 polyester
C15	220p polystyrene
C16	100µ 10V elect
C17	3n3 polyester
C18	4n7 polyester
C19	330p polystyrene
C20	10µ 25V elect

Semiconductors

IC1	LF351N
IC2	LF351N
IC3	4046BE
IC4	4001BE
IC5	LF351N
IC6	LF351N
TR1	BC549
TR2	BC549
TR3	BC549
D1	MFOE71, or SFH750
D2	MFOD71

Miscellaneous

| JK1 | 3.5mm jack socket |
| JK2 | 3.5mm jack socket |

Cases, circuit boards, 8 pin DIL IC holder (off), 14 pin DIL IC holder, 16 pin DIL IC holder, fibre-optic cable, wire, solder, etc.

Altered values and additional components (Fig. 2.15)

R10 3k9
TR4 SFH350

P.W.M. Audio Link

A p.w.m. system is the main alternative to using an f.m. type. This is another form of digital link, but in its standard form a fixed carrier frequency is used. The audio signal is modulated onto the fixed frequency carrier wave in the form of a varying mark-space ratio. The block diagram of Figure 2.16 helps to explain the way in which this method functions.

The audio input signal is fed to one input of a voltage comparator via a lowpass filter. The audio signal is modulated onto a carrier signal at an ultrasonic frequency (about 80kHz in this case), and the purpose of the lowpass filter is to remove any high frequency input signals that could otherwise react with the carrier signal to produce heterodyne tones on the output signal. In many cases there will be no significant high frequency content on the input signal anyway, but it is as well to include this filter just in case. Stray pick up of radio signals by the input wiring can sometimes give problems if the lowpass filtering is omitted.

A clock oscillator drives the other input of the comparator, and this oscillator provides a triangular output waveform. The clock signal must have good linearity, as any lack of linearity here will produce distortion on the audio output signal. This arrangement gives the required pulse width modulation, and the waveforms of Figure 2.17 show the way in which the modulation process operates. In Figure 2.17(a) the audio input to the comparator is at its normal quiescent level, which is half way between the peak voltages of the clock signal. The output of the comparator goes high when the input signal is above the clock potential, and low when the input signal is below the clock voltage. This gives a squarewave output signal having a perfect 1 to 1 mark-space ratio, and the average output voltage is equal to half the supply voltage.

In Figure 2.17(b) the input level is much higher, and as a result of this the clock signal exceeds to input voltage during only a small part of each clock cycle. This produces much longer output pulses, and the average output voltage is proportionately higher. The input level is very low in Figure 2.17(c), and the clock signal is at a higher voltage than the input signal for the majority of the time. This results in an output signal that is a series of short pulses, having a low average output voltage.

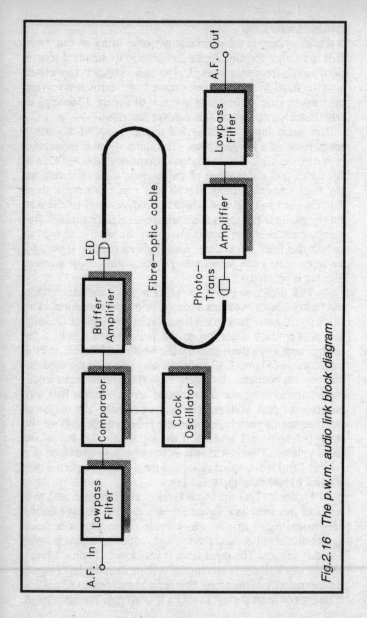

Fig.2.16 The p.w.m. audio link block diagram

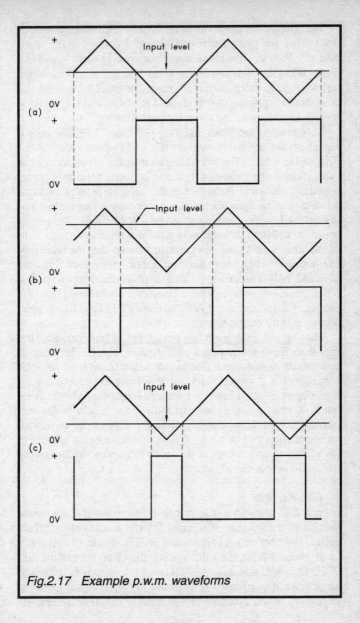

Fig.2.17 Example p.w.m. waveforms

The important point to note is that the average output voltage of the comparator can altered by varying the input voltage. Provided the clock signal has good linearity, there is a linear relationship between the input voltage and the average output voltage from the comparator. In order to convert the comparator's pulsing output signal back to an audio signal it is merely necessary to use some lowpass filtering.

Returning to the block diagram of Figure 2.16, the output signal of the comparator drives the LED at the input of the fibre-optic cable. The phototransistor at the other end of the cable detects the pulses of light and converts them into corresponding electrical pulses. On the face of it there is some advantage in using a photodiode rather than a phototransistor, due to the higher operating speed of a photodiode. This extra speed would help to accurately maintain the mark-space ratio of the processed signal. In practice I found that the relatively low sensitivity of a photodiode produced unusable results, and I would only recommend using a phototransistor with this p.w.m. link. An amplifier stage boosts the output level from the phototransistor and also speeds up the signal to produce a good quality p.w.m. output signal.

This is fed through a lowpass filter which smooths the signal to leave the required audio output signal. In order to produce an output signal that has an insignificant level of clock breakthrough it is necessary for this filter to provide a very high degree of attenuation at the clock frequency. On the other hand, it must not significantly roll-off the higher audio frequencies. This means that a high slope filter must be used, with an attenuation rate of about 40dB per octave being needed to give 80dB of attenuation at the clock frequency, while leaving the audio output signal intact.

P.W.M. Circuits

Figure 2.18 shows the full circuit diagram for the modulator section of the system. The input filter is a conventional third order (18db per octave) type based on IC3. Its cutoff frequency is at about 20kHz, and the system therefore covers the full 20Hz to 20kHz audio range. VR1 sets the input bias level, and in practice it is adjusted to optimise the large signal handling capability of the system. This is more a matter of setting the

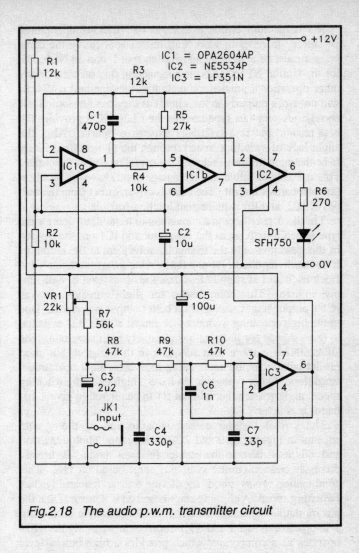

Fig.2.18 *The audio p.w.m. transmitter circuit*

optimum bias level for the comparator than for the filter, and the comparator is driven directly from the output of IC3.

IC2 is the comparator, and this is an NE5534P operational amplifier. In order to work well in this application the comparator must be able to switch at high speed, and an NE5534P (or the similar NE5534AN) is adequate in this respect. Many other operational amplifiers, including the standard µA741C, will not work properly in this circuit as they can not switch fast enough. A very fast type such as the EL2045CN provides the best results, but is a relatively expensive option. Also, the slight lack of switching speed through the photocells is likely to be the main limiting factor on the overall speed of the circuit. This is likely to dilute any advantage contributed by an ultra-fast comparator circuit. The LED is driven direct from the output of IC2, and R6 is its current limiting resistor.

The clock oscillator is a conventional triangular/squarewave type which uses IC1a as the integrator and IC1b as the trigger. In this case it is only the triangular waveform at the output of IC1a that is required. R1 and R2 provide a bias voltage for the clock oscillator at slightly less than the usual level of half supply voltage. This compensates for slight non-symmetry in IC1's output stages, and gives a better output waveform. Due to the high operating frequency of almost 80kHz it is essential to use a device for IC1 that has a suitably high slew rate. The OPA2604AP is more than adequate in this respect, but good results will not be obtained using most other dual operational amplifiers. Other types that do have a high enough switching speed might require the value of R1 to be altered to give a different bias level.

The circuit for the demodulator section of the system appears in Figures 2.19 and 2.20. TR1 is the phototransistor, and it is used here in the emitter follower mode. It directly drives a common emitter switching stage based on TR2. This combination gives good sensitivity and a reasonably fast switching speed. A clipping stage based on IC4 ensures that the p.w.m. output signal switches at a suitably fast rate even when a long cable is used and TR1 receives a weak signal. IC4 operates as a comparator which provides a high output level when the collector of TR2 is at more than half the supply voltage, and a low output level when it is at less than half the supply potential. VR2 is adjusted so that the p.w.m. output from IC4 accurately matches that from the transmitter.

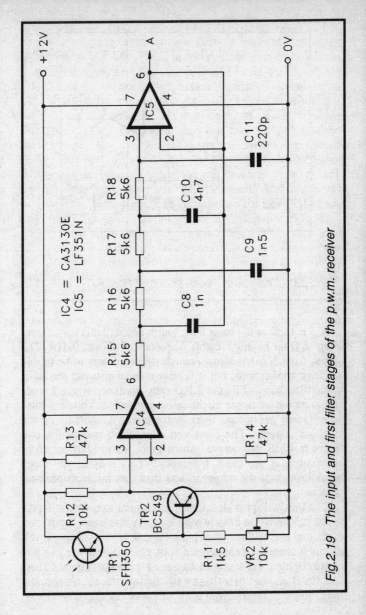

Fig.2.19 The input and first filter stages of the p.w.m. receiver

51

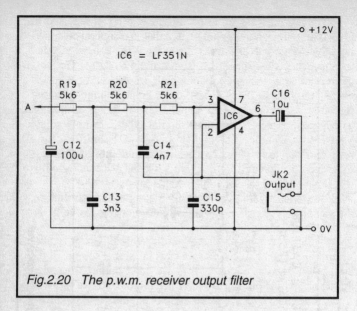

Fig.2.20   The p.w.m. receiver output filter

IC5 is used as the basis for a fourth order (24dB per octave) lowpass filter having a cutoff frequency of about 20kHz. The output from IC5 has a low enough ripple content to be usable in many applications, but it is advisable to also use the additional filter stage of Figure 2.20 in any situations where a moderate amount of ripple might cause problems. This is a third order (18dB per octave) filter, again having a cutoff frequency at about 20kHz. The combined attenuation rate of the two filters is 42dB per octave, which gives about 80dB or so of attenuation at the clock frequency. This reduces the clock breakthrough at the output to less than one millivolt peak-to-peak.

The unit will provide an excellent signal to noise ratio provided it is driven at a fairly high level. A maximum input level of around one to three volts peak-to-peak is ideal. Input levels of much more than about three volts peak to peak are likely to cause clipping and severe distortion of the output signal. There is a small amount of voltage gain through the circuit incidentally, and the output signal is about double the input level.

If you have access to an oscilloscope, VR1 is adjusted to give an output signal at pin 6 of IC2 that is a squarewave having an accurate 1 to 1 mark-space ratio. VR2 is then adjusted to give an accurate squarewave signal at pin 6 of IC4. If access to an oscilloscope is not possible, both presets can be adjusted using a multimeter that will read the average voltage when fed with a high frequency pulse signal. This includes all normal analogue multimeters, and most digital types. Simply adjust VR1 for a reading of 5.5 volts at pin 6 of IC2, and VR2 for a reading of 5.5 volts at pin 6 of IC4. If you do not have access to any test equipment, simply give VR1 and VR2 any settings that provide good results at high signal levels.

While this system does not provide super-fi performance, the signal to noise ratio is excellent and it covers virtually the full audio bandwidth. The distortion performance is quite good, and the system produced no discernible loss of quality when using a good quality FM tuner as the signal source. If the system exhibits a poor signal to noise ratio, this indicates that an abnormally weak signal is getting through to the receiver. You should then check that the cable is in good working order, and that it is connected to the photocells reliably.

Components for P.W.M. Audio Link
(Figs. 2.18, 2.19 and 2.20)

Resistors (all 0.25 watt 5% carbon film)

R1	12k
R2	10k
R3	12k
R4	10k
R5	27k
R6	270R
R7	56k
R8	47k
R9	47k
R10	47k
R11	1k5
R12	10k
R13	47k
R14	47k

R15 to R21	5k6 (7 off)

Potentiometers

VR1	22k min preset
VR2	10k min preset

Capacitors

C1	470p polystyrene
C2	10µ 25V elect
C3	2µ2 50V elect
C4	330p polystyrene
C5	100µ 16V elect
C6	1n polyester
C7	33p polystyrene
C8	1n polyester
C9	1n5 polyester
C10	4n7 polyester
C11	220p polystyrene
C12	100µ 16V elect
C13	3n3 polyester
C14	4n7 polyester
C15	330p polystyrene
C16	10µ 25V elect

Semiconductors

IC1	OPA2604AP
IC2	NE5534P
IC3	LF351N
IC4	CA3130E
IC5	LF351N
IC6	LF351N
D1	SFH750
TR1	SFH350
TR2	BC549

Miscellaneous

JK1	3.5mm jack socket
JK2	3.5mm jack socket

Cases, circuit board, 8 pin DIL IC holder (6 off), fibre-optic cable, wire, solder, etc.

D.C. P.W.M. Link

It is possible to use an f.m. system or a p.w.m. type in situations where a d.c. link is required. A p.w.m. system is the usual choice, and the audio p.w.m. link is easily modified for use with d.c. levels. Figure 2.21 shows the modified transmitter circuit. The input voltage is provided by VR2, but the input signal could be provided by something like a temperature sensor, provided its output voltage is within the range 0 to 11 volts. Simply omit VR2 and connect the input signal to the bottom end of R5.

Ideally the clock signal would have a peak-to-peak voltage equal to the supply potential. The average output voltage would then be identical to the input voltage. Failing that, the clock signal should reach 0 volts on negative peaks, so that the average output voltage would be smaller than but proportional to the input potential. The value of R4 is only a little higher than that of R3, which gives a high output voltage swing from IC1a. However, the clock signal still has an amplitude that is something less than the full supply potential. This is not of major importance, since VR1 can be adjusted to provide a minimum clock voltage that is virtually at 0 volts.

In practice it is unlikely that there will be no offset voltage at all through the link. In other words, as the input voltage is increased above zero, at first the output voltage will fail to increase. It will then increase at the appropriate rate, but will always be slightly short of the correct value. In this case the offset can be reduced to a matter of millivolts, which in many applications will be insignificant. The linearity of the system is very good, and is much better than that of the simple d.c. link described previously.

A wide bandwidth is not normally of any importance with a d.c. link, since the input voltage is never likely to vary at anything other than a "snails pace". Good linearity is usually of much greater consequence. Accordingly, it is better to use a relatively low clock frequency so that the comparatively narrow bandwidth of the system does not impede linearity, even at very high and low input voltages. In this case the clock frequency is about 2.7kHz, which gives good linearity but still enables the unit to adjust to changes in the input voltage in only a few milliseconds.

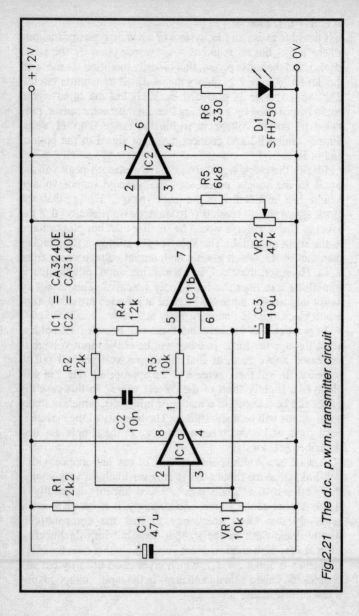

Fig.2.21 The d.c. p.w.m. transmitter circuit

56

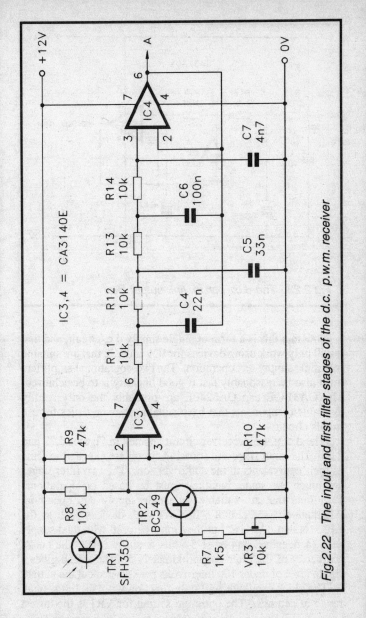

Fig.2.22 The input and first filter stages of the d.c. p.w.m. receiver

57

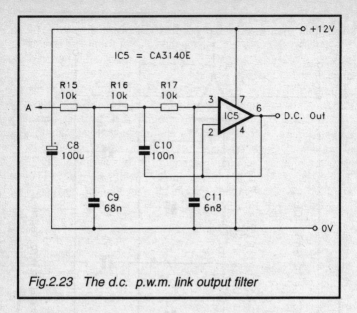

Fig.2.23   The d.c. p.w.m. link output filter

Note that this is a form of single supply d.c. circuit, and that it will only work using devices for IC1 and IC2 that are suitable for single supply d.c. operation. The two operational amplifiers must also be reasonably fast if good linearity is to be achieved. The CA3140E and CA3240E are probably the only readily available components that have suitable characteristics for use in this circuit.

The d.c. p.w.m. receiver circuit appears in Figures 2.22 and 2.23. The input stage and squaring circuit are exactly the same as their equivalents in the audio version. The two filter stages are much the same, but they must be based on operational amplifiers that are suitable for single supply d.c. operation. Alternatively, the circuit will work with devices such as the LF351N and uA741C, but they must be used with dual supply rails (a negative supply of 5 volts is sufficient). The cutoff frequency of the filter is approximately 500Hz, which gives a ripple level of under 100 microvolts peak-to-peak at the output.

The clock oscillator will only function with VR1 at a small range of settings. The optimum setting for VR1 is the lowest wiper voltage that provides reliable oscillation. It is just possible that the circuit will fail to oscillate reliably at any setting of VR1. If this should occur, raising the value of R4 to 13k should cure the problem. Alternatively, add a resistor of a few hundred ohms in value in series with R4.

If an oscilloscope is available, set VR2 to produce an accurate squarewave signal at the output of IC2 (pin 6). Then adjust VR3 for an accurate squarewave at pin 6 of IC3. If access to an oscilloscope is not possible, a multimeter that can read the average voltage of a pulsed signal can be used instead. Adjust VR2 for an average output potential of 6 volts at pin 6 of IC2. Then adjust VR3 for an output voltage of 6 volts from IC5. The output from the receiver should then track the input voltage from VR2 with good accuracy.

Components for D.C. P.W.M. Link (Figs. 2.21, 2.22 and 2.23)

Resistors (all 0.25 watt 5% carbon film)

R1	2k2
R2	12k
R3	10k
R4	12k
R5	6k8
R6	330R
R7	1k5
R8	10k
R9	47k
R10	47k
R11 to R17	10k (7 off)

Potentiometers

VR1	10k min preset
VR2	47k lin carbon
VR3	10k min preset

Capacitors

C1	47µ 16V elect
C2	10n polyester
C3	10µ 25V elect
C4	22n polyester

C5	33n polyester
C6	100n polyester
C7	4n7 polyester
C8	100μ 16V elect
C9	68n polyester
C10	100n polyester
C11	6n8 polyester

Semiconductors

IC1	CA3240E
IC2 to IC5	CA3140E (4 off)
D1	SFH750
TR1	SFH350
TR2	BC549

Miscellaneous

Cases, circuit boards, control knob, 8 pin DIL IC holder (5 off), fibre-optic cable, wire, solder, etc.

P.W.M. Motor Controller

A p.w.m. system is probably the best choice if you require speed control of a small d.c. electric motor via a fibre-optic cable. There is no need to use any filtering at the receiver, because small d.c. electric motors work well when powered from a pulse signal, provided the signal is not at a very high or very low frequency. It is generally accepted that a p.w.m. signal provides more precise control of a small d.c. motor than a simple variable voltage, because the motor is fully switched on during the periods when an output pulse is present. This helps to nudge the motor into action at start-up, giving smooth control from a standing start. Using a simple variable voltage controller the motor usually starts rather jerkily. Resistance to stalling, particularly at slow speeds, also tends to be much better using a p.w.m. controller.

Figure 2.24 shows the circuit for the transmitter section of the fibre-optic p.w.m. motor controller. This is just a slightly revamped version of the p.w.m. d.c. link described previously. In this case there is no need to arrange the circuit to minimise problems with the offset voltage. Instead, speed control VR1 is

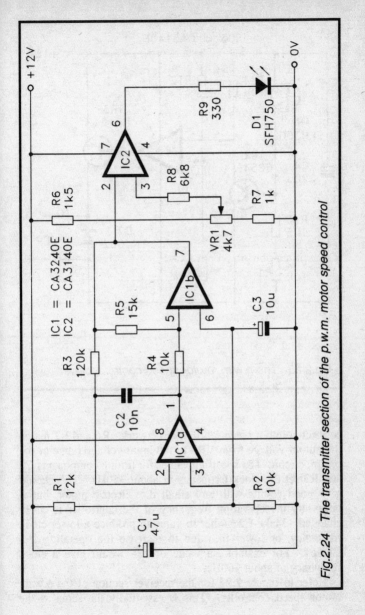

Fig.2.24 The transmitter section of the p.w.m. motor speed control

61

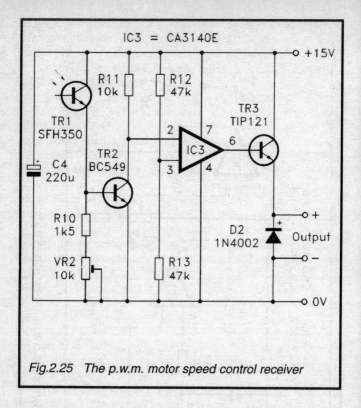

Fig.2.25   The p.w.m. motor speed control receiver

connected into a potential divider network. R6 and R7 match the output voltage from VR1 to the input voltage range of the p.w.m. circuit. The specified values for timing components C2 and R3 set the clock frequency at about 350Hz. This should give good results with any small d.c. electric motor, but if necessary the operating frequency of the controller is easily changed. Make C2 higher in value to produce a lower clock frequency, or lower in value to increase the operating frequency. For example, a value of 22n would give a clock frequency of about 160Hz.

Refer to Figure 2.25 for the receiver section of the p.w.m. motor speed controller. This is essentially the same as the receiver section of d.c. p.w.m. link, but with the lowpass filtering omitted. Instead, the output of IC3 is used to drive an emitter follower buffer amplifier (TR3). This is actually a darlington power device, and it is able to handle output currents of an amp or two. D2 suppresses any reverse voltage spikes that are generated across the highly inductive load provided by a d.c. motor.

The circuit is powered from a 15 volt supply, but due to the inevitable voltage drop through TR3 the maximum output voltage is about 12 volts. The controller is therefore suitable for use with any 12 volt d.c. electric motor that draws no more than about 2 amps when loaded. The supply should be reasonably stable and free from large amounts of ripple. The receiver circuit does not incorporate output current limiting, but in many cases the circuit will be powered from a mains power supply unit that provides current limiting. My preferred way of doing things is to power a circuit of this type from a power supply unit based on a 15 volt monolithic voltage regulator. The regulator should be a one or two amp type, depending on the power rating of the motor used with the controller.

If the receiver is powered from a supply unit that does not include current limiting, it would be better to use the slightly modified receiver circuit of Figure 2.26. TR4 and R14 provide a conventional current limiting action, and protect the circuit against short term overloads (including short circuits across the output). Long term overloads could cause TR3 to overheat unless it is fitted on a suitably large heatsink. The specified value for R14 sets the maximum output current at a little over one amp. For a maximum output current of 2 amps reduce the value of R14 to 0.33 ohms. R14 should have a power rating of 1 watt (2 watts if a 0.33 ohm component is used).

Although TR3 operates in a switching mode, it still has to dissipate a few watts when the circuit is run at or near maximum power. TR3 must therefore be mounted on a medium sized heatsink. One having a rating of about 6 degrees Celsius per watt should be perfectly adequate. Note that the collector leadout of TR3 connects internally to its heat-tab. Where appropriate, TR3 must be insulated from the heatsink using a standard TO220 insulating kit. When constructing the unit remember that all three integrated circuits are static-sensitive, and that they therefore require the standard anti-static handling precautions. VR2 is simply given any setting that enables proper control of the motor using VR1. A bit of trial and error is all that is needed in order to find a suitable setting.

Components for P.W.M. D.C. Motor Controller
(Figs. 2.24 and 2.25)

Resistors (all 0.25 watt 5% carbon film)

R1	12k
R2	10k
R3	120k
R4	10k
R5	15k
R6	1k5
R7	1k
R8	6k8
R9	330R
R10	1k5
R11	10k
R12	47k
R13	47k

Potentiometers

VR1	4k7 lin carbon
VR2	10k min preset

Capacitors

C1	47µ 16V elect
C2	10n polyester
C3	10µ 25V elect
C4	220µ 25V elect

Semiconductors

IC1	CA3240E
IC2	CA3140E
IC3	CA3140E
D1	SFH750
D2	1N4002
TR1	SFH350

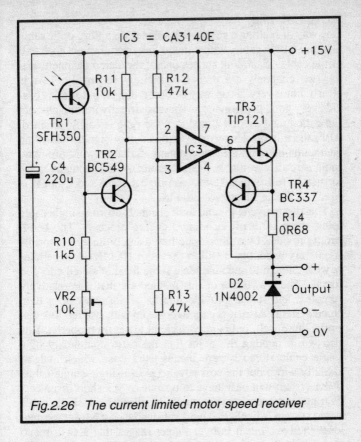

Fig.2.26 The current limited motor speed receiver

| TR2 | BC549 |
| TR3 | TIP121 or TIP122 |

Miscellaneous
Cases, circuit boards, control knob, 8 pin DIL IC holder (3 off), fibre-optic cable, heatsink for TR3 (see text), wire, solder, etc.

Additional components for Fig. 2.26
| R14 | OR68 (power rating see text) |
| TR4 | BC337 |

Stereo F.M. Link

One way of sending a stereo audio signal via a fibre-optic cable is to use a twin cable, with a mono link operating via each half of the cable. Each link carries one of the stereo channels, and the two channels are processed entirely separately. This is clearly not a very cheap way of doing things, but it does provide very good performance. There is virtually infinite channel separation, and a good signal to noise ratio is easily obtained. Also, there is no danger of spurious output signals due to an interaction between the two channels. Suitable twin fibre-optic cable is readily available (RS/Electromail). It is actually made for use in full duplex (two way) digital serial links, but it is equally suitable for stereo audio use.

The alternative is to send both channels down a single cable using some form of encoding/decoding process. The bandwidth provided by a fibre-optic link using ordinary photocells is not very wide, but is still in excess of 100kHz. It is certainly wide enough to accommodate some form of stereo encoded signal. The drawbacks of this method are that it is relatively complex, and it will provide inferior performance to a twin mono system. Also, it is easy to come up with a stereo link that works quite well, but is very difficult to set up properly. It is also worth making the point that the extra complexity of a single cable stereo system means extra cost, which at least partially wipes out the cost advantage of using a single cable. If the system will only have to operate over a short distance a twin mono system might actually be cheaper. A single cable stereo system is likely to have a substantial cost advantage over longer ranges, but it is over longer ranges that a twin mono system will have the greatest performance advantage.

My preference is to use a twin mono system to provide a stereo link. The superior performance is generally worth the extra cost. On the other hand, a single cable stereo link represents a more interesting approach, and has more appeal to the electronics experimenter. The single cable stereo link described here does not require the use of any test equipment or complex procedures in order to get it "up and running". Even so, it is not a beginners project, and is included only for the benefit of readers who are suitably experienced at electronic project construction. The transmitter and receiver circuits are both rather more complex than the projects featured previously, and they will be considered separately, starting with the transmitter.

Transmitter

Figure 2.27 shows the block diagram for the stereo transmitter. The system is an f.m. type, and the basic function of the transmitter is to generate two frequency modulated carrier waves on significantly different frequencies. The lower carrier frequency is just under 60kHz, and the higher carrier frequency is about 95kHz. With the mono f.m. system it was satisfactory to use a squarewave output signal, but this does not work well with a stereo system. Mixing two squarewave carrier signals together seems to generate a wide range of output frequencies, which makes it virtually impossible to filter out two "clean" carrier signals at the receiver. The carrier signals must therefore be reasonably pure sinewave signals.

The initial stages are duplicated in the stereo channels, and consist of an input buffer stage, a lowpass filter, a v.c.o. (voltage controlled oscillator), and a further lowpass filter. The buffer is used to ensure that the filter is driven from a suitably low source impedance, and the filtering removes any high frequency input signals that might otherwise react with the carrier signals to generate heterodyne whistles. The v.c.o.s produces the frequency modulated carrier waves, but they provide squarewave output signals. These are filtered by the lowpass filters to greatly attenuate the harmonics, so that reasonably pure sinewave signals are left. These are combined in a conventional mixer circuit, and then fed to the LED via a buffer stage.

Figure 2.28 shows the circuit diagram for the input stages of the left hand channel. IC1 is used as the buffer stage at the input, and this provides an input impedance of about 50k. The lowpass filter is a third order (18dB per octave) type based on IC2. Its cutoff frequency is approximately 20kHz. The output of IC2 is direct coupled to the control input of the v.c.o. This uses a 4046BE, which is the same device that is used in the mono f.m. audio link. VR1 is the tuning control, and this is set for an output frequency of about 95kHz. In practice it is simply adjusted for optimum results from the left hand channel

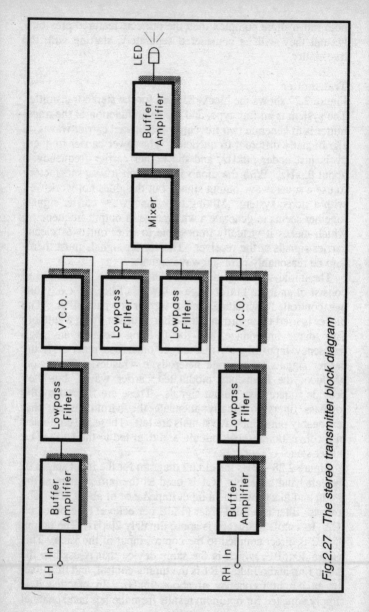

Fig.2.27 The stereo transmitter block diagram

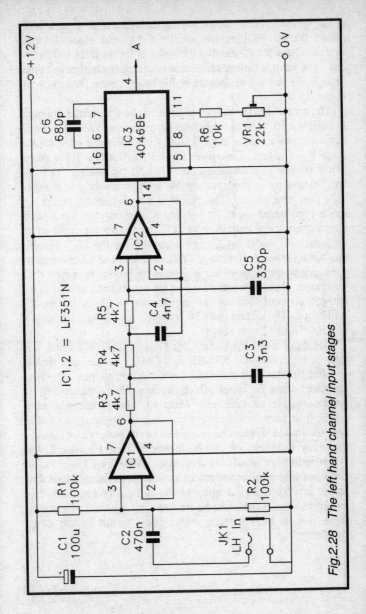

Fig.2.28   The left hand channel input stages

of the system, and no frequency meter is required. Figure 2.29 shows the circuit diagram for the right hand channel input stages. These are essentially the same as for the left hand channel. The v.c.o.'s timing resistance is somewhat higher in value though, so that it can operate at the lower centre frequency of about 60kHz.

The circuit for the output section of the transmitter appears in Figure 2.30. The two lowpass filters are passive types, each consisting of a single stage L – C filter followed by a single stage R – C filter. This gives what are effectively three stage filters having an attenuation rate of 18dB per octave. The filters "cleans up" the output signals sufficiently to give reasonably pure sinewaves. The mixer is a conventional summing mode type based on IC7. I found it necessary to use a high speed operational amplifier for IC7 since other types failed to perform well under load, even when driving the LED via the emitter follower buffer stage (TR1). If you use an alternative operational amplifier in the IC7 position it must be a type that will work well at frequencies of up to 100kHz or so. The current consumption of the transmitter is about 20 to 25 milliamps. The circuit must be powered from a well smoothed and stabilised 12 volt supply.

Construction of the transmitter is quite straightforward, but bear in mind that the 4046BE is a CMOS device, and that it requires the standard anti-static handling precautions. The two inductors must be types which work well at frequencies of around 40kHz to 120kHz. Most r.f. chokes are not very efficient at such low frequencies. For an application of this type the inductors must be wound on ferrite pot cores, or one of the many variations on this basic type of core. I used the type 10RB inductors which are available from Cirkit Distribution Ltd., but any similar inductors should be suitable. Note that ferrite is very hard but quite brittle and easily smashed. The inductors should therefore be treated with due care. Dropping them onto a hard surface could easily result in the cores smashing.

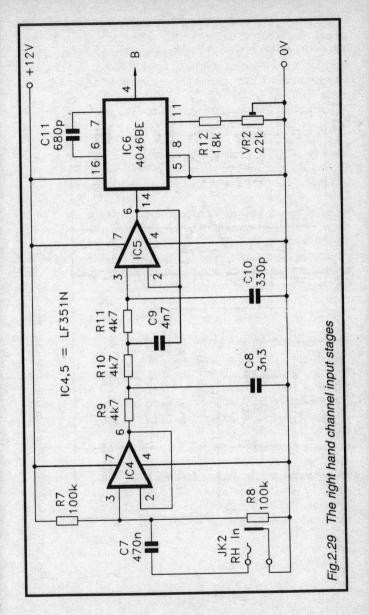

Fig.2.29 The right hand channel input stages

71

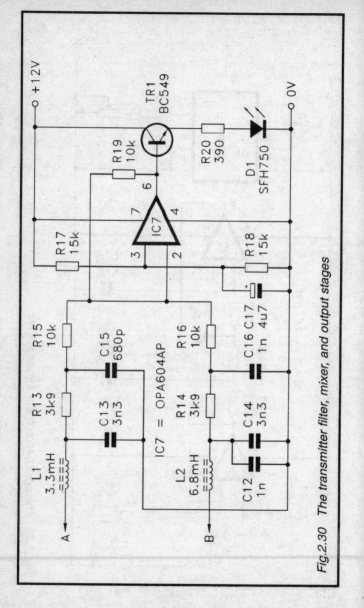

Fig.2.30 The transmitter filter, mixer, and output stages

Components for Stereo F.M. Transmitter
(Figs. 2.28, 2.29 and 2.30)

Resistors (all 0.25 watt 5% carbon film)

R1	100k
R2	100k
R3	4k7
R4	4k7
R5	4k7
R6	10k
R7	100k
R8	100k
R9	4k7
R10	4k7
R11	4k7
R12	18k
R13	3k9
R14	3k9
R15	10k
R16	10k
R17	15k
R18	15k
R19	10k
R20	390R

Potentiometers

VR1	22k min preset
VR2	22k min preset

Capacitors

C1	100µ 16V elect
C2	470n polyester
C3	3n3 polyester
C4	4n7 polyester
C5	330p polystyrene
C6	680p polystyrene
C7	470n polyester
C8	3n3 polyester
C9	4n7 polyester
C10	330p polystyrene

C11	680p polystyrene
C12	1n polyester
C13	3n3 polyester
C14	3n3 polyester
C15	680p polystyrene
C16	1n polyester
C17	4µ7 50V elect

Semiconductors

IC1	LF351N
IC2	LF351N
IC3	4046BE
IC4	LF351N
IC5	LF351N
IC6	4046BE
IC7	OPA604AP
TR1	BC549
D1	SFH750

Miscellaneous

JK1	3.5mm jack socket
JK2	3.5mm jack socket
L1	3.3mH
L2	6.8mH

Case, circuit board, 8 pin DIL IC holder (5 off), 16 pin DIL IC holder (2 off), fibre-optic cable, wire, solder, etc.

Receiver

The block diagram for the stereo f.m. receiver is shown in Figure 2.31. The output signal from the phototransistor is split two ways. The two signal paths are essentially the same, but operate over different frequency bands. The first stage in each case is a preamplifier. These are followed by bandpass filters which extract the carrier signals, and remove other signals. One operates at about 60kHz and extracts the right hand channel carrier wave, and the other operates at about 95kHz and extracts the left hand channel carrier signal. In order to obtain adequate separation of the two carrier signals it is necessary to resort to a second bandpass filter in each channel, with a buffer stage between each pair of filters.

74

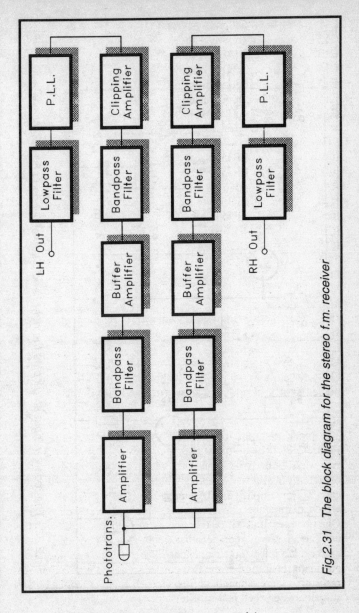

Fig.2.31   The block diagram for the stereo f.m. receiver

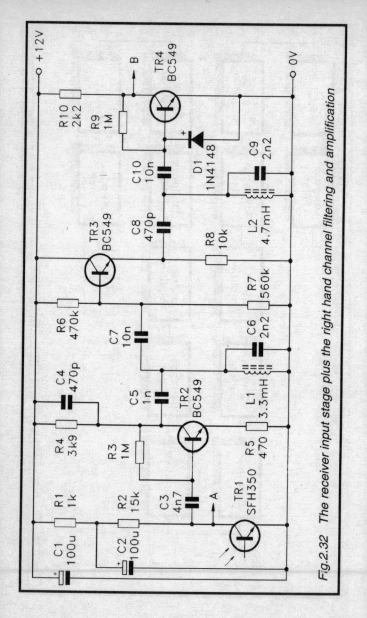

Fig.2.32   The receiver input stage plus the right hand channel filtering and amplification

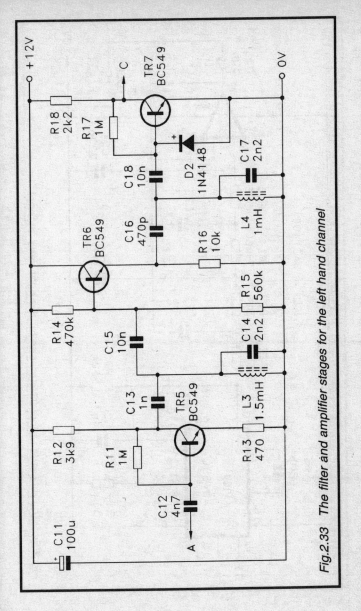

Fig.2.33 The filter and amplifier stages for the left hand channel

77

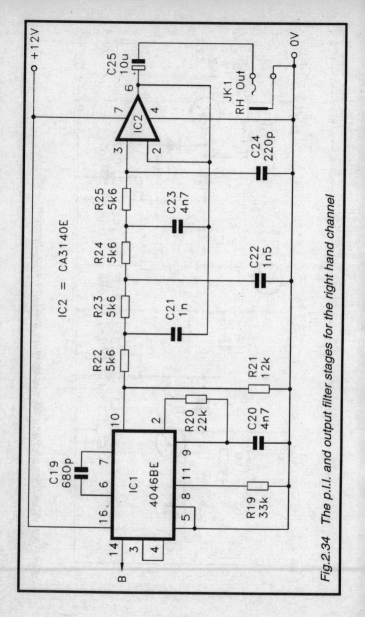

Fig.2.34 The p.l.l. and output filter stages for the right hand channel

78

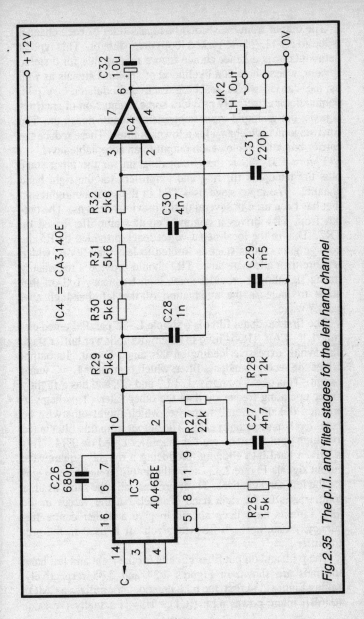

Fig.2.35 The p.l.l. and filter stages for the left hand channel

The output from the second bandpass filter of each channel is fed to a p.l.l. (phase locked loop) demodulator. This type of demodulator is a better choice than a monostable for a stereo system, where there is a likelihood of spurious signals as well as the carrier waves reaching each demodulator. A p.l.l. demodulator effectively provides some attenuation of spurious signals, but a simple monostable demodulator does not. The final stage in each channel is a lowpass filter. These reduce the carrier breakthrough on each output to an acceptable level.

Figure 2.32 shows the circuit diagram for the input stage plus the bandpass filtering and amplifiers for the right hand channel. The input stage uses TR1 in the same configuration that has been used in several of the previous designs. The output from TR1 drives a common emitter amplifier based on TR2. Due to the local negative feedback provided by R5 the voltage gain of this stage is limited to less than 20dB, which is more than adequate since TR2 should provide a reasonably strong signal. C4 provides some high frequency roll-off that helps to increase the attenuation of the left hand channel carrier wave.

The first bandpass filter is a simple L – C parallel tuned circuit (L1 – C6). TR3 is used in an emitter follower buffer stage that avoids excessive loading on this tuned circuit. Its output drives the second bandpass filter, which is another L – C tuned circuit. This one is comprised of L2 and C9, and has a slightly lower operating frequency than the other filter. This helps to broaden out the overall response, which might otherwise be excessively narrow and peaky. The output from this filter is fed to a high gain common emitter amplifier based on TR4. This is driven hard into clipping, producing a roughly squarewave output signal. Figure 2.33 shows the amplifier and filter stages for the left hand channel. These are basically the same as their counterparts in the right hand channel, but the values in the filter circuits have been altered to give a higher centre frequency. Also, no high frequency roll-off is used in the pre-amplifier.

The p.l.l. and output filter circuits for the right and left hand channels are shown in Figures 2.34 and 2.35 respectively. Taking Figure 2.34 first, the p.l.l. demodulator utilizes a CMOS 4046BE micro-power p.l.l. (IC1). This is actually the same chip that is used in each of the modulators, but in this case more than just the v.c.o. section is used. R20 and C20 form the low-pass filter between the output of the phase comparator and the input of the v.c.o. The 4046BE actually has two phase comparators, and the output of the other comparator is available at pin 13. The circuit will operate using either phase comparator, but the one having its output at pin 2 seems to provide significantly better results. In particular, it provides an audio output signal that is much more free from spurious signals. The output from the lowpass filter constitutes the demodulated audio signal. It is extracted via an integral source follower buffer stage of IC1. R21 is the discrete load resistor for this stage.

In order to provide a really low ripple content on the output signal it is necessary to use some further lowpass filtering. This filtering is provided by a four stage (24dB per octave) filter based on IC2. Together with the filtering in the p.l.l. itself this gives an attenuation rate of 30dB per octave. The lowpass filters in the transmitter and receiver give virtually the full audio bandwidth, with the only exception of the filter in the p.l.l. This does roll-off the high frequency response of the system slightly, but this will not be of any great consequence in many applications. If necessary, C20 could be made somewhat lower in value in order to reduce the high frequency roll-off. However, if C20 is made much lower in value the p.l.l. may fail to hold lock correctly. I have not tried it, but using pre-emphasis at the transmitter would probably be a better solution. In other words, use complementary treble boost at the transmitter to counteract the treble cut at the receiver.

The circuit for the left hand channel only differs from that for the right hand channel in that the timing resistor in the v.c.o. (R26) has been made lower in value. This tunes the v.c.o. higher in frequency so that it can lock onto the higher carrier frequency used for the left hand channel.

Building the receiver does not present any major problems, but it would be advisable to use a component layout that keeps the two channels reasonably well separated. Also, bear in mind that the 4046BE chips are CMOS types, and that they therefore require the normal anti-static handling precautions. Like the inductors in the transmitter, the inductors used in the receiver must be a type intended for operation at around 40 to 120kHz, such as the Cirkit type 10RB. A little trial and error is needed in order to get the whole system up and running, but it should not be difficult to find suitable settings for the two tuning presets at the transmitter. The input signal level should be at about one to two volts peak-to-peak. The output level from the receiver will be at a somewhat lower level than this incidentally.

Components for Stereo F.M. Receiver
(Figs. 2.32, 2.33, 2.34 and 2.35)

Resistors (all 0.25 watt 5% carbon film)

R1	1k
R2	15k
R3	1M
R4	3k9
R5	470R
R6	470k
R7	560k
R8	10k
R9	1M
R10	2k2
R11	1M
R12	3k9
R13	470R
R14	470k
R15	560k
R16	10k
R17	1M
R18	2k2
R19	33k
R20	22k
R21	12k
R22	5k6
R23	5k6
R24	5k6
R25	5k6
R26	15k

R27	22k
R28	12k
R29	5k6
R30	5k6
R31	5k6
R32	5k6

Capacitors

C1	100µ 16V elect
C2	100µ 16V elect
C3	4n7 polyester
C4	470p polystyrene
C5	1n polyester
C6	2n2 polyester
C7	10n polyester
C8	470p polystyrene
C9	2n2 polyester
C10	10n polyester
C11	100µ 16V elect
C12	4n7 polyester
C13	1n polyester
C14	2n2 polyester
C15	10n polyester
C16	470p polystyrene
C17	2n2 polyester
C18	10n polyester
C19	680p polystyrene
C20	4n7 polyester
C21	1n polyester
C22	1n5 polyester
C23	4n7 polyester
C24	220p polystyrene
C25	10µ 25V elect
C26	680p polystyrene
C27	4n7 polyester
C28	1n polyester
C29	1n5 polyester
C30	4n7 polyester
C31	220p polystyrene
C32	10µ 25V elect

Semiconductors

IC1	4046BE
IC2	CA3140E
IC3	4046BE
IC4	CA3140E
TR1	SFH350
TR2 to TR7	BC549 (6 off)
D1	1N4148
D2	1N4148

Miscellaneous

L1	3.3mH
L2	4.7mH
L3	1.5mH
L4	1mH
JK1	3.5mm jack socket
JK2	3.5mm jack socket

Case, circuit board, 8 pin DIL IC holder (2 off), 16 pin DIL IC holder (2 off), wire, solder, etc.

The type 10RB inductors are available from:

Cirkit Distribution Ltd.,
Park Lane,
Broxbourne,
Herts.,
EN10 7BR.
(Tel. 01992 448899)

Chapter 3

DATA LINKS

Fibre-optic links between computers (and other pieces of digital equipment) are becoming quite commonplace. There are actually quite a few ready-made units and modules intended for this type of thing. Some are designed to handle ordinary RS232C serial signals, while others can handle high speed serial data. Unfortunately, most of these ready-made systems and modules are too expensive for the average electronics experimenter to "play" with. However, building your own RS232C optical link is a reasonably inexpensive exercise, and very simple circuits can provide excellent results.

D.C. Link

There are two main approaches to sending digital data down a fibre-optic cable. The least complex of the two is to use a simple direct coupled system. The alternative is to use an f.s.k. (frequency shift keying) system. We will consider both types here, starting with a simple direct coupled system. Figure 3.1 shows the block diagram for a data link of this type.

The transmitter is extremely simple, and is basically just an electronic switch driving the LED at an appropriate current. When the input signal is high the LED is switched on – when it is low the LED is switched off. At the receiver a photo-transistor drives an amplifier stage, and for the system to work properly the output of the amplifier must provide a voltage swing of a few volts peak to peak. On the other hand, as the circuit is direct coupled throughout, only a moderate amount of gain can be used here as there will otherwise be problems with drift. The system is therefore dependent on a reasonably strong signal reaching the receiver, which tends to limit the maximum range of a d.c. system. I found that a range of about 20 metres was possible, but a range much in excess of this would probably only be achievable using a very efficient photocell/cable combination. Of course, for most requirements a range of up to about 20 metres is more than sufficient.

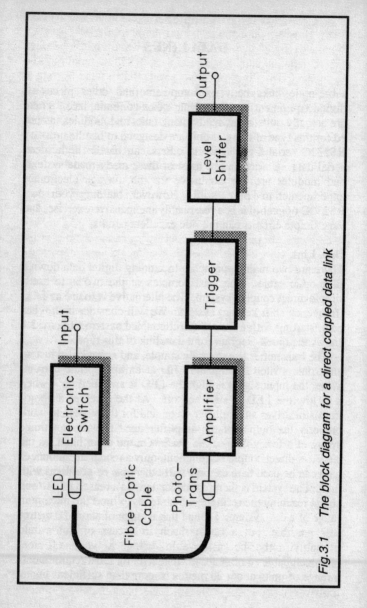

Fig.3.1   The block diagram for a direct coupled data link

The next stage in the receiver is a trigger circuit which effectively clips the output signal from the amplifier to provide a logic style signal that switches "cleanly" and rapidly between virtually the full supply rail potentials. RS232C serial links do not operate using ordinary logic levels, but instead operate at nominal signal levels of plus and minus 12 volts. Minimum loaded signal potentials of plus and minus 3 volts are required. Despite the theoretical requirements, most RS232C inputs can actually be driven successfully without resorting to negative signals levels. However, in order to be sure that the serial input port is driven properly it is necessary to use a suitable level shifter circuit at the output of the receiver. In practice there is no difficulty in combining this circuit with the trigger stage.

As the system is effectively d.c. coupled from the input of the transmitter to the output of the receiver, it will operate well with low baud rate serial signals. However long the bits of the input signal may happen to be, the system will accurately maintain the mark-space ratio of the input signal. At the other end of the frequency range a simple d.c. system can easily handle signals at the highest normal baud rate of 19200 baud. Such a signal has a maximum fundamental frequency of 9.6kHz, which is well within the capabilities of the photocells provided the phototransistor receives a reasonably strong signal. A weak signal would result in the phototransistor operating at a very low current, which would provide a relatively limited bandwidth.

D.C. Link Circuits
Figure 3.2 shows the circuit diagram for the d.c. data link transmitter. This is basically just a simple common emitter switch driving the LED (D2) via current limiter R3. The circuit will work from a 5 volt supply, but the value of R3 should be reduced to 100 ohms in order to maintain the LED's "on" current at about 30 milliamps.

Refer to Figure 3.3 for the circuit diagram of the d.c. link receiver. TR2 is the phototransistor, and it operates in the emitter follower mode. I did not manage to obtain satisfactory results using a photodiode in this type of circuit, and would only recommend the use of a reasonably sensitive phototransistor such as the SFH350. The phototransistor directly

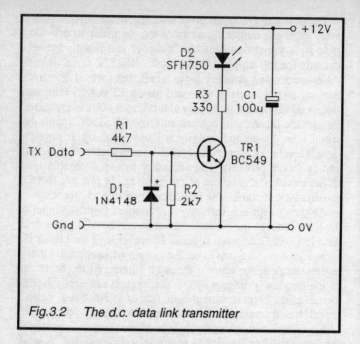

Fig.3.2   The d.c. data link transmitter

drives a common emitter amplifier based on TR3. VR1 controls the sensitivity of the circuit, and in use this is adjusted to give an output signal having a mark-space ratio that accurately mimics the serial input signal.

IC1 is an operational amplifier, but in this circuit it is used as a voltage comparator. R6 and R7 provide a reference potential of half the supply voltage to the non-inverting input of IC1. When TR3's collector goes above this voltage the output of IC1 goes low, and when TR3's collector goes below the reference level IC1's output goes high. The level shifting is obtained simply by powering IC1 from dual balanced 12 volt supplies. The signal undergoes various inversions through the link, but the output from IC1 is in-phase with the input signal, and can be read properly by an RS232C input port.

As pointed out previously, most RS232C input ports can be driven properly without using a negative signal voltage. Most ports will work perfectly well if a low signal level is

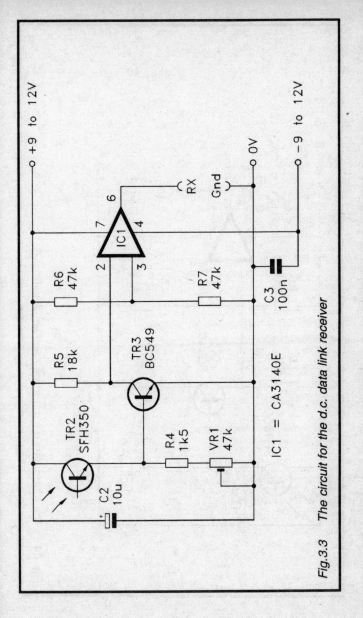

Fig.3.3   The circuit for the d.c. data link receiver

89

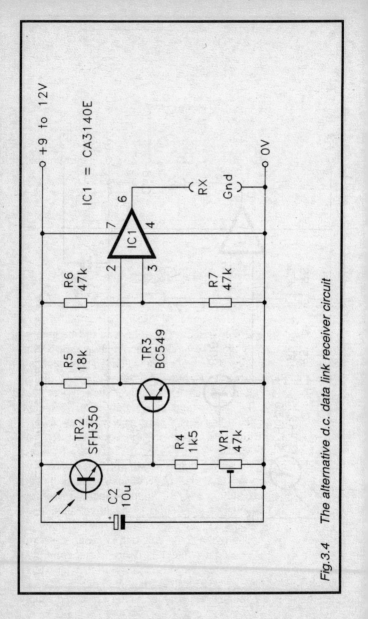

Fig.3.4 The alternative d.c. data link receiver circuit

90

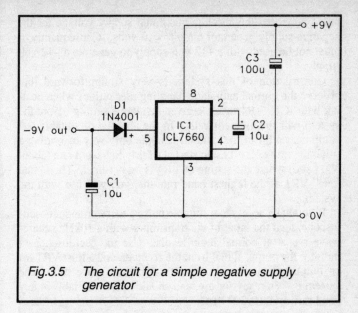

Fig.3.5   The circuit for a simple negative supply generator

represented by a 0 volt signal level. This can not be guaranteed, and it is only likely to work if the receiver unit is connected to the RS232C port via a cable which is no more than a few metres long. The only way to ascertain whether or not this method will work reliably is to use the "suck it and see" method. Figure 3.4 shows the single supply receiver circuit. Note that the device used for IC1 must be a type that can provide a minimum output voltage virtually equal to the 0 volt supply potential. Most types (LF351N, μA741C, etc.) will not work properly in the single supply version of the receiver.

If the dual supply version of the receiver is needed in order to obtain reliable results, a negative supply generator may represent the easiest way of providing the negative supply rail. Figure 3.5 shows the circuit for a simple negative supply generator that will provide a –9 volt output from a +9 volt supply. The loaded output voltage is likely to fall some way short of a genuine –9 volts, but this circuit will provide a high enough voltage to give good results from the d.c. link receiver. The circuit is not reliant on having accurately matched supply rails. Note that the absolute maximum supply voltage for the negative supply generator circuit is 10 volts. Consequently, it must not be used with a +12 volt supply to generate a −12 volt supply.

Construction of this system is very straightforward, but observe the normal anti-static handling precautions when dealing with IC1. VR1 must be given a suitable setting before the system will function correctly. In the absence of suitable test equipment a bit of trial and error is the only way of finding a suitable setting. It is best to start at a fairly low baud rate (about 300 baud) where the setting of VR1 is less critical. Then "fine tune" VR1 at the highest baud rate that you will use with the system.

If you have access to a suitable pulse generator and an oscilloscope, feed the input of the transmitter with a 10kHz square-wave signal at normal logic levels. Use the oscilloscope to monitor the output signal from the receiver, and adjust VR1 for an output signal having a one-to-one mark-space ratio. The system is then ready for use, and should operate reliably at any baud rate up to 19200 baud.

Connections
A single transmitter/receiver provides only a basic half-duplex link with no handshaking. Further links could be used to implement hardware handshaking, but this is not the normal approach to the problem. One method is to simply send the data at a modest baud rate so that there is no risk of the receiving device becoming overloaded with data. Where this method is inappropriate it is normal to implement a full duplex system (i.e. two links, one for use in each direction). Software handshaking (also known as "X-on/X-off" handshaking) should then be selected. This uses codes sent over the data link to control the flow of data. A system of this type can provide handshaking with data being exchanged in either direction. Twin fibre-optic cable for use in full duplex systems is readily available (RS/Electromail).

A common problem when attempting to send data over a fibre-optic link is that of the sending device refusing to transmit data. Fortunately, the receiving device refusing to accept data is relatively rare, so if the transmitting device can be

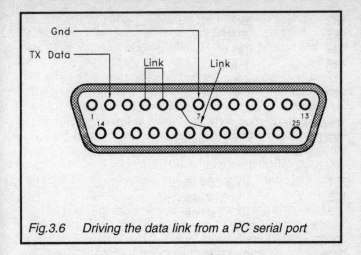

Fig.3.6   Driving the data link from a PC serial port

persuaded to send the data, the receiving device will almost certainly accept it, and the link should have been established correctly. The problem seems to be due to handshake inputs on the transmitting device "floating" to the wrong logic level. If left unconnected the handshake inputs often drift to the state that provides a hold-off. This should not really be a problem if software handshaking has been selected, but in practice it might be a problem with either type of handshaking activated.

If there is no apparent way of setting up the port to ignore the handshake inputs, connecting them to the port's handshake outputs will usually solve the problem. This results in the handshake inputs being held in the state that enables a flow of data from the port. Figure 3.6 shows a method of linking that I have found to work well with PC serial ports, but the same basic approach should work with practically any serial port that has handshake outputs (or a +12 volt terminal that can be used to "pull" handshake lines high). The links are from RTS to CTS (pin 4 to pin 5), and from DSR to DTR (pin 6 to pin 20).

Components for D.C. Data Link (Figs. 3.2 and 3.3)

Resistors (all 0.25 watt 5% carbon film)
R1   4k7

R2	2k7
R3	330R
R4	1k5
R5	18k
R6	47k
R7	47k

Potentiometer

| VR1 | 47k min preset |

Capacitors

C1	100µ 16V elect
C2	10µ 25V elect
C3	100n ceramic

Semiconductors

IC1	CA3140E
TR1	BC549
TR2	SFH350
TR3	BC549
D1	1N4148
D2	SFH750

Miscellaneous

Cases, circuit boards, fibre-optic cable, RS232C connectors
and leads, 8 pin DIL IC holder, wire, solder, etc.

Components for Negative Supply Generator (Fig. 3.5)

Capacitors

C1	10µ 25V elect
C2	10µ 25V elect
C3	100µ 25V elect

Semiconductors

| D1 | 1N4001 |
| IC1 | ICL7660 |

F.S.K. Link

An f.s.k. data link uses a.c. coupling, and can therefore use relatively high gain at the receiver in order to obtain increased range. Since a d.c. coupled link can provide sufficient range for most purposes, this is not necessarily a particularly great advantage in the current context. Perhaps of greater importance, it is not essential to obtain a strong signal at the receiver in order to obtain reliable operation of the system. If a cable is connected to one of the photocells with something considerably less than 100 percent efficiency, the link will probably continue to function normally. A d.c. coupled system is rather less accommodating. Particularly when used over longer ranges, a d.c. link will only operate reliably if everything is set up correctly, and properly maintained.

An f.s.k. system is the digital equivalent of an f.m. audio link. The high and low logic levels are encoded in the form of two different carrier frequencies. This is basically the same system that is used with modems to send computer data via the telephone system. The block diagram of Figure 3.7 helps to explain the way in which this f.s.k. data link operates.

The transmitter is based on a v.c.o. (voltage controlled oscillator). The input signal drives an electronic switch which is used to shift the v.c.o. between its two carrier frequencies. In order for the system to function properly the carrier frequency must always be at least double the maximum input frequency. In this case the maximum fundamental input frequency is 9.6kHz, which means that the carrier frequency should not be less than about 20kHz. In order to avoid problems with complex filtering at the receiver it is necessary to use a minimum carrier frequency that is much higher than 20kHz. In this system the carrier frequencies are approximately 110kHz and 220kHz. This is just about within the bandwidth of the photocells, and is high enough to make the receiver relatively straightforward. The output from the v.c.o. drives the LED via a buffer amplifier.

The input and demodulator stages of the receiver are much the same as those in the audio f.m. receiver. The output from the phototransistor is boosted by a high gain amplifier. Next the signal is fed to a monostable, and the output from this stage is fed to a lowpass filter. This smooths the monostable's

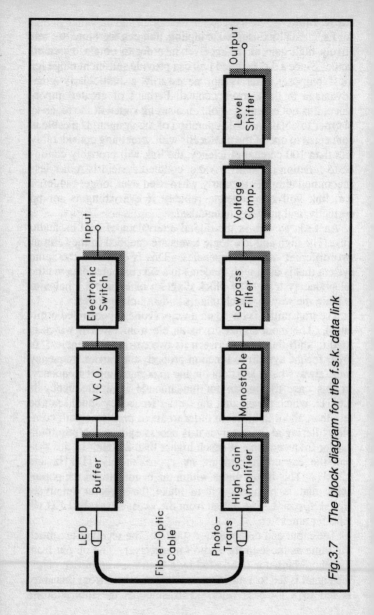

Fig.3.7 The block diagram for the f.s.k. data link

output pulses to give a demodulated output signal, which in this case is a sort of pseudo logic signal switching between two voltages. A voltage comparator stage processes this signal to produce a "clean" and fast switching signal that is more like a true logic signal. A level shifter stage boosts this signal to one at standard RS232C levels that will drive a serial input port correctly. Like the d.c. system, the last two stages of the f.s.k. receiver can be combined into a single circuit that provides both triggering and level shifting.

F.S.K. Circuits

The circuit diagram for the f.s.k. transmitter appears in Figure 3.8. TR1 is used as a common emitter switch at the input of the circuit. The v.c.o. is based on the oscillator section of a 4046BE micro-power phase locked loop, and this is basically the same as the v.c.o. used in the audio f.m. transmitter circuit described previously. Under standby conditions TR1 is switched off, and the control voltage for the v.c.o. is provided by R3 and R5. As R3 is much lower in value than R5, the control voltage is a fairly high portion of the supply voltage. In fact it is about 8.5 volts, and this gives the higher carrier frequency of approximately 220kHz. When the input signal goes high, TR1 switches on, and R4 is shunted across R5. This reduces the control voltage to about half its previous level, and reduces the carrier frequency to around 110kHz.

The LED (D2) is driven from the output of IC1 via TR2, which operates as an emitter follower buffer stage. R7 sets the "on" LED current at about 30 milliamps, but the squarewave drive signal results in an average LED current of around 15 milliamps. The current consumption of the circuit as a whole is only fractionally higher than this.

Figure 3.9 shows the circuit diagram for the amplifier and monostable stages of the f.s.k. receiver. The circuit diagram for the lowpass filter and output stage appears in Figure 3.10. There was an instability problem with the original version of the receiver. The problem seemed to be at least partially due to stray feedback to the unconnected base terminal of TR3. Connecting the base lead of TR3 to the 0 volt supply rail seems to provide greatly improved stability, but it also significantly reduces the sensitivity of TR3. However, the sensitivity of the

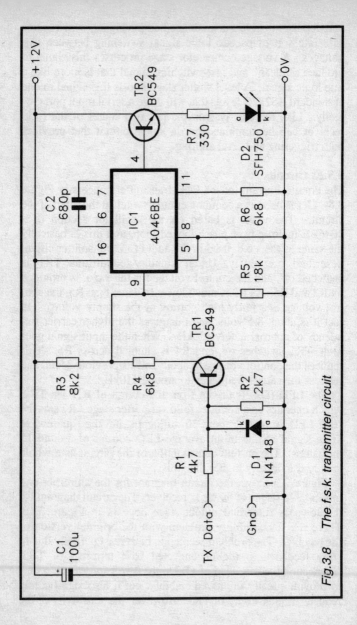

Fig.3.8 The f.s.k. transmitter circuit

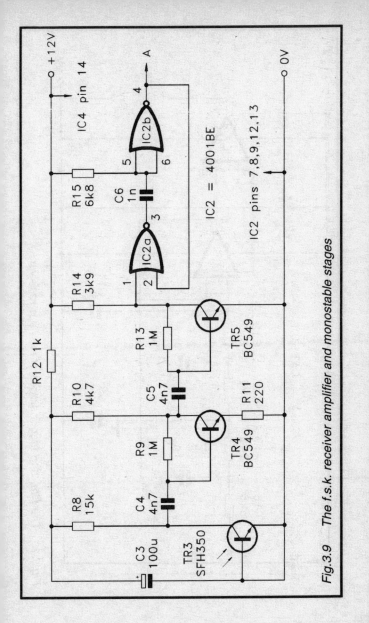

Fig.3.9 The f.s.k. receiver amplifier and monostable stages

99

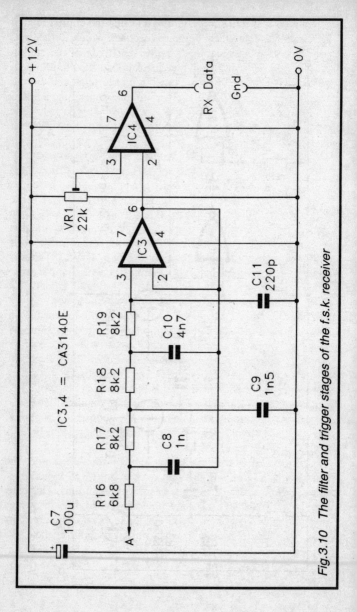

Fig.3.10 The filter and trigger stages of the f.s.k. receiver

100

receiver is still quite good. Adding R11 into the emitter lead of TR4 provides some local negative feedback which further aids good stability. This also reduces the sensitivity of the circuit, but only marginally since the feedback boosts the input impedance of TR4 and reduces the loading on the photocell circuit. The monostable is based on two of the gates in a CMOS 4001BE quad 2 input NOR gate package. This is much the same as the monostable used in the audio f.m. receiver described in Chapter 2.

The high carrier frequencies make it possible to use relatively simple filtering in the receiver. The lowpass filtering is provided by a fourth order (24dB per octave) filter based on IC3. This has its cutoff frequency at approximately 15kHz, which is high enough to give good results at baud rates of up to 19200, but is low enough to give a large amount of attenuation at the lower carrier frequency. The output from IC3 drives a simple voltage comparator circuit based on IC4. VR1 is adjusted to give an output signal having a mark-space ratio that accurately matches the mark-space ratio of the input signal. IC4 does not provide negative output voltages, but if necessary it can be made to do so by using a –12 volt supply (as for IC2 in Figure 3.3). The current consumption of the circuit is around 8 to 10 milliamps.

It is possible to use a photodiode rather than a phototransistor, as shown in Figure 3.11. It is just a matter of connecting the diode in the reverse bias mode in place of TR3, and no other modifications to the circuit are required. The sensitivity of the circuit seems to be quite good using a photodiode, which should be well able to handle the relatively high carrier frequencies in use here.

Construction of the system should be reasonably simple, but remember that all the integrated circuits are MOS input types that require the usual anti-static handling precautions. Due care should be taken to avoid any obvious feedback paths when designing the component layout for the receiver. The notes on setting up and using the d.c. data link also apply to the f.s.k. system.

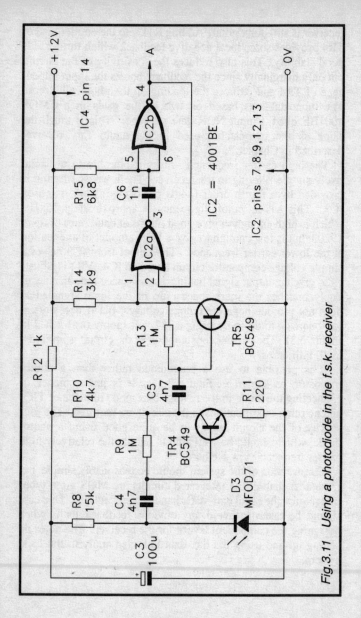

Fig.3.11 Using a photodiode in the f.s.k. receiver

102

Components for F.S.K. Data Link
(Figs. 3.8, 3.9, 3.10 and 3.11)

Resistors (all 0.25 watt 5% carbon film)

R1	4k7
R2	2k7
R3	8k2
R4	6k8
R5	18k
R6	6k8
R7	330R
R8	15k
R9	1M
R10	4k7
R11	220R
R12	1k
R13	1M
R14	3k9
R15	6k8
R16	6k8
R17	8k2
R18	8k2
R19	8k2

Potentiometer

VR1	22k min preset

Capacitors

C1	100µ 16V elect
C2	680p polystyrene
C3	100µ 16V elect
C4	4n7 polyester
C5	4n7 polyester
C6	1n polyester
C7	100µ 16V elect
C8	1n polyester
C9	1n5 polyester
C10	4n7 polyester
C11	220p polystyrene

Semiconductors

IC1	4046BE
IC2	4001BE
IC3	CA3140E
IC4	CA3140E
TR1	BC549
TR2	BC549
TR3	SFH350
TR4	BC549
TR5	BC549
D1	1N4148
D2	SFH750
D3	MFOD71 (see text)

Miscellaneous

Cases, circuit boards, fibre-optic cable, RS232C connectors and leads, 8 pin DIL IC holder (2 off), 14 pin DIL IC holder, 16 pin DIL IC holder, wire, solder, etc.

MIDI Link

MIDI (musical instruments digital interface) is now the standard method of external control for electronic musical instruments, and it is even used with some of the more major accessories such as digital effects units. From the hardware point of view MIDI is basically just a standard serial system, much like an RS232C interface. However, it differs from the RS232C system in a couple of important respects. One of these is simply that it uses a non-standard baud rate of 31250 baud, which is substantially higher than the maximum RS232C baud rate of 19200 baud. It is still well within the capabilities of a simple fibre-optic link though.

The main difference is that MIDI operates using a 5 milliamp current loop, with an opto-isolator at every input. In other words, a MIDI output is driven by an open collector transistor, and each input has an opto-isolator with its LED driven at a current of 5 milliamps when the transistor is switched on. This method helps to avoid problems with "hum" loops, digital noise being coupled into the audio signal path, etc. The data links described so far are unsuitable for use with

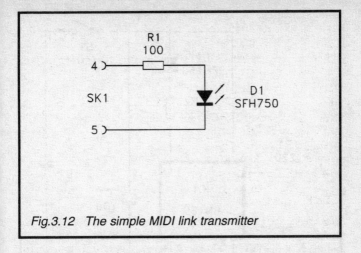

Fig.3.12 The simple MIDI link transmitter

MIDI equipment because they are incompatible with the 5 milliamp current loop system.

It is not difficult to adapt the d.c. data link for operation with MIDI systems. The transmitter can consist of nothing more than a LED and series resistor, as shown In Figure 3.12. One slight drawback of this method is that it only provides a relatively limited LED current. The value of the current limiting resistor has been made slightly lower than normal in order to boost the LED current slightly, but it is still unlikely to be more than about 6 to 7 milliamps. This is adequate for an operating range of about 5 to 8 metres, but it is unlikely to give acceptable results using a cable much longer than this.

Improved results can be obtained using the transmitter circuit of Figure 3.13. This is based on a 6N139 opto-isolator, which is a high quality type. At its input there is the usual infra-red LED, and R1 provides part of the current limiting for this LED (the rest is provided by the MIDI output that drives the circuit). On the output side of the component there is a photodiode, an emitter follower buffer stage, and a common emitter switching transistor. This gives the combination of high speed and good efficiency that are essential in this application. R3 is the load resistor for the emitter follower stage. D1 is driven from the open collector output stage of IC1 via

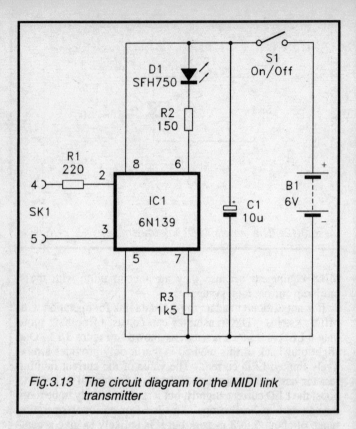

Fig.3.13 The circuit diagram for the MIDI link transmitter

current limiting resistor R2. The "on" LED current is about 27 milliamps, but the average LED current is always substantially less than this. In fact it is never likely to be more than about half this value. A range of 20 metres or so is easily achieved using this transmitter circuit.

Figure 3.14 shows the circuit diagram for the MIDI link receiver. This is basically just a slightly modified version of the d.c. data link's input stages. The load resistor for TR2 has been omitted, and instead the LED in the opto-isolator is driven by TR2 via current limiting resistors R5 and R6. VR1 must be adjusted to give an output signal that accurately follows the input signal. The easiest way of doing this is to connect two

106

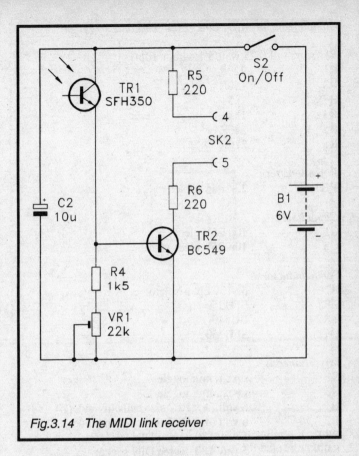

Fig.3.14 The MIDI link receiver

instruments together using this link, and then use trial and error to find a setting for VR1 that results in the slave unit correctly mimicking the master instrument. The setting of VR1 will be quite critical if only a weak signal is reaching the receiver. Standard 5 way DIN MIDI leads are used to connect the MIDI output of the master instrument to SK1, and SK2 to the MIDI input of the slave instrument. The current consumption of the receiver circuit is negligible under standby conditions, and is no more than a two or three milliamps at times of high MIDI activity.

Components for MIDI Link (Figs. 3.13 and 3.14)

Resistors (all 0.25 watt 5% carbon film)
R1	220R
R2	150R
R3	1k5
R4	1k5
R5	220R
R6	220R

Potentiometer
VR1	22k min preset

Capacitors
C1	10µ 25V elect
C2	10µ 25V elect

Semiconductors
IC1	6N139 opto-isolator
TR1	SFH350
TR2	BC549
D1	SFH750

Miscellaneous
S1	s.p.s.t. min toggle
S2	s.p.s.t. min toggle
B1	6 volt (4 × HP7 size cells in holder)
B2	6 volt (4 × HP7 size cells in holder)
SK1	5 way 180 degree DIN socket
SK2	5 way 180 degree DIN socket

Cases, circuit boards, 8 pin DIL IC holder, PP3 battery connector (2 off), fibre-optic cable, wire, solder, etc.

Chapter 4

POTPOURRI

In this chapter we will consider a few fibre-optic projects that are not concerned with audio links, data links, or any form of control. The first of these miscellaneous projects is a simple loop alarm. An alarm of this type is used for protecting goods that are on display in a shop (or on a market stall), and conventionally the loop is a loop of wire. The alarm works along the general lines shown in Figure 4.1, where the loop of wire is threaded through the handles of the items to be protected. The latter could be some transistor radios, handbags, bracelets, or anything that can be threaded onto the piece of wire. The wire is connected into a simple circuit that operates an audible alarm if someone cuts the wire in attempt to steal some of the protected items.

An alarm of this type is quite effective, but a determined thief could defeat the alarm by bypassing part of the loop before cutting the wire and making off with the spoils. A loop alarm which uses a fibre-optic cable rather than a simple piece of wire is slightly more expensive, but is virtually "uncrackable". Electrically bypassing a piece of wire, even while it is carrying a signal, is quite easy, but bypassing a fibre-optic cable is extremely difficult. While it is probably technically feasible, bypassing a fibre-optic cable is very difficult in practice. Trying it would almost certainly trigger the alarm, and anyone undertaking intricate tampering with the cable would soon be spotted anyway.

D.C. Alarm

In its most simple form a fibre-optic alarm uses a non-modulated signal through the cable. Figure 4.2 shows the block diagram for a simple d.c. coupled loop alarm of this type. The transmitter is very simple, and merely consists of a power source which drives the LED at a fairly high current so that it provides high brightness. At the receiver a phototransistor and a d.c. amplifier provide an output level that is normally low. If the fibre-optic cable is cut, the light level to the phototransistor

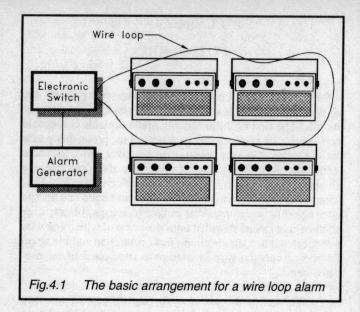

Fig.4.1   The basic arrangement for a wire loop alarm

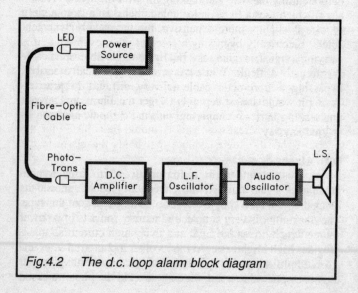

Fig.4.2   The d.c. loop alarm block diagram

is reduced, and the output from the d.c. amplifier goes high. This activates a low frequency oscillator, which in turn activates an audio oscillator. The latter drives a loudspeaker, and the bursts of tone from the audio oscillator produce a "beep-beep-beep" type alarm sound.

There is an obvious flaw in this arrangement in that the ambient light level might be high enough to hold the alarm in the quiescent state. In practice the ambient light level would probably not be high enough to do this, but it would not be a good idea to use this version of the alarm in a situation where there might be a high level of ambient light (out-of-doors on a bright sunny day for example). There is another potential flaw in that someone could block the alarm by shining a bright light into the appropriate cut end of the cable. This is not very likely though, as they would need to know how the alarm works, and which piece of cable to feed from the light source. Anyway, the alarm would almost certainly sound for a short time before the light source could be put into place, which should be sufficient to alert the shop or stall holder.

Figure 4.3 shows the full circuit diagram for the d.c. loop alarm. D1 is the LED and R1 is its current limiting resistor. The LED current is about 20 milliamps. This is high enough to give good LED brightness, but is within the maximum current rating of any normal LED.

The receiver has TR1 and TR2 in much the same arrangement that was utilized in several of the projects described previously. The specified value for R2 gives reasonable sensitivity, and the circuit should work using a cable of up to about 8 metres in length. For optimum results R2 should be replaced with a 10k preset resistor. This is should be adjusted for the lowest sensitivity (lowest value) that holds the alarm in the "off" state under standby conditions.

The alarm generator is based on two 555 gated astable circuits. IC1 is used in the low frequency oscillator, and its operating frequency is a little under 3Hz. The gate signal is applied to pin 4, which is actually the reset input. However, it functions well as a gate input, and switches off the oscillator if it is held below approximately 0.5 volts. IC2 is used in exactly the same configuration, but its timing component values set the operating frequency at a little under 2kHz. LS1 is a cased

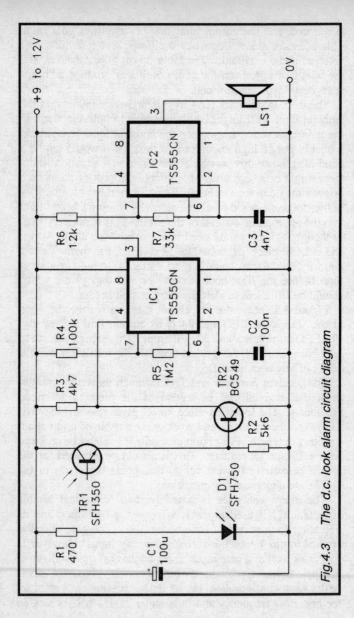

Fig.4.3   The d.c. look alarm circuit diagram

112

ceramic resonator, and a component of this type provides good efficiency at this fairly high audio frequency. Note that LS1 should only be ceramic resonator, and not an ordinary moving coil loudspeaker. Trying to use a moving coil loudspeaker with this circuit could result in IC2 being damaged, and it would be unlikely to provide a good alarm sound. The typical current consumption of the circuit is slightly in excess of 20 milliamps.

The cased ceramic resonator will probably have red and black flying leads, but it can in fact be connected with either polarity. IC1 and IC2 can be any low power versions of the 555 timer. The circuit should also work if standard 555s are used, but the current consumption will be about 15 milliamps higher. Low power versions of the 555 are mostly based on CMOS technology, but they have static protection circuits that render any special handling precautions unnecessary.

Testing the completed unit is very simple. With the cable fitted to the photocells the alarm should not sound. Disconnecting the cable from one of the photocells should result in the "beep-beep-beep" alarm sound being produced immediately. If the alarm sounds even when the cable is in position, try the system with a very short piece of cable. If it works correctly with a short cable, then the problem is that the longer cable is not providing enough light to the photocell. Raising the value of R2 would probably correct this, but it would also increase the risk of the ambient light level holding the alarm in the "off" state. It would be better to settle for a slightly shorter cable.

Components for D.C. Loop Alarm (Fig.4.3)

Resistors (all 0.25 watt 5% carbon film)

R1	470R
R2	5k6
R3	4k7
R4	100k
R5	1M2
R6	12k
R7	33k

Capacitors
C1   100µ 16V elect
C2   100n polyester
C3   4n7 polyester

Semiconductors
IC1   TS555CN or similar
IC2   TS555CN or similar
TR1   SFH350
TR2   BC549
D1   SFH750

Miscellaneous
LS1   Cased ceramic resonator
Case, circuit board, fibre-optic cable, 8 pin DIL IC holder (2 off), wire, solder, etc.

Modulated Loop Alarm

Greater reliability can be obtained from a fibre-optic loop alarm by using some form of modulated light source. It would be possible to use complex modulation, plus a receiver circuit that would detect even slight corruption of the signal. In practice there is no real point in going to such lengths, since even a simple amplitude modulated signal is sufficient to render the unit impervious to the ambient light level, and virtually "uncrackable".

Figure 4.4 shows the block diagram for the modulated fibre-optic loop alarm. The transmitter consists of an oscillator driving the LED. The exact operating frequency of the oscillator is unimportant, and anything from a middle audio frequency to an ultrasonic frequency will provide good results. At the receiver the output from the phototransistor is amplified, and then the signal is smoothed and rectified. This gives a strong positive d.c. output signal provided the signal from the transmitter is received properly.

The output from the smoothing circuit drives an electronic switch, which in turn controls an alarm generator that is the same as the one used in the d.c. loop alarm. The alarm is held in the "off" state when a suitably strong signal is received from

114

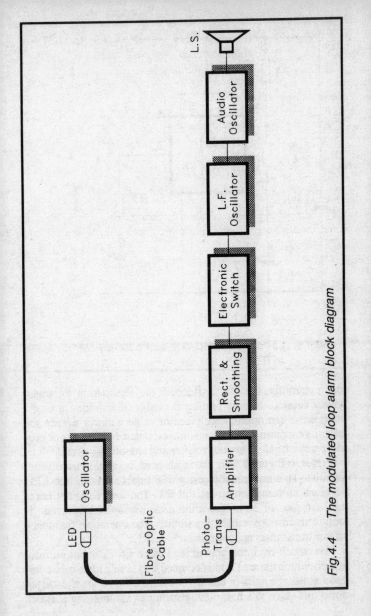

Fig.4.4   The modulated loop alarm block diagram

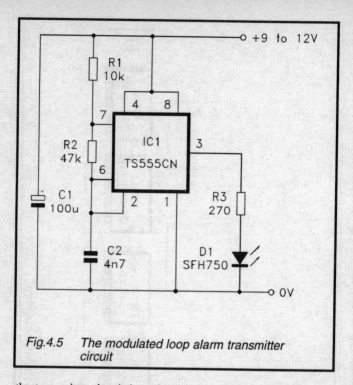

Fig.4.5   The modulated loop alarm transmitter
           circuit

the transmitter, but it is activated if the signal from the transmitter ceases. Simply cutting the cable and shining a bright
light down the appropriate piece of cable will not silence the
alarm generator, because a non-modulated light will not produce any output from the rectifier and smoothing circuit.

Refer to Figure 4.5 for the modulated loop alarm transmitter
circuit. This is basically just a 555 astable driving the LED
(D1) via current limiting resistor R3. The "on" LED current is
in the region of 30 milliamps, but the average LED current is
only a fraction over half this figure. The operating frequency
of the transmitter is approximately 1.4kHz.

The receiver circuit appears in Figure 4.6. The output from
the phototransistor (TR1) is coupled by C3 to a high gain common emitter amplifier based on TR2. C4 couples the output
from this stage to a half-wave rectifier and smoothing network

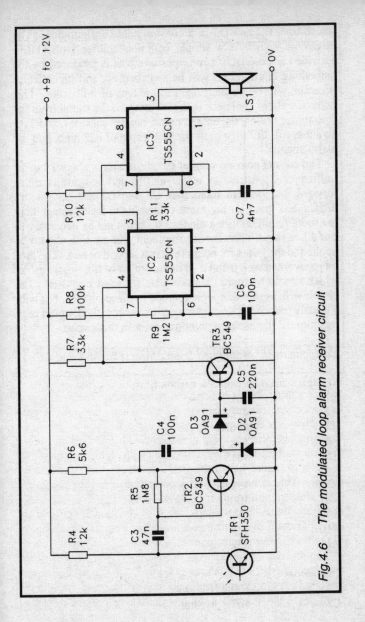

Fig.4.6   The modulated loop alarm receiver circuit

117

which uses D2 and D3 in a conventional configuration. The electronic switch is a simple common emitter type (TR3). Provided a reasonably strong positive bias is produced by the smoothing circuit, TR3 will be switched on, and its collector potential will be no more than a few tens of millivolts. This holds the alarm generator in the off state. If the signal from the transmitter ceases, the charge on C5 rapidly subsides, and TR3 switches off. R7 then pulls the reset input of IC2 high, and the alarm sounds.

The current consumption of the entire unit is about 17 to 20 milliamps. Construction of the unit should be quite straight-forward, but bear in mind that D2 and D3 are germanium diodes, and that they are more vulnerable to heat damage than the more familiar silicon diodes. It should not be necessary to use a heatshunt when connecting them, but the iron should be applied to the joints for no more than a second or two. The prototype worked well using a 20 metre length of fibre-optic cable, which should be more than adequate for most purposes. The circuit will work using a photodiode in place of TR1, but with a greatly reduced operating range. Consequently, I would only recommend the use of a phototransistor in this circuit.

Components for Modulated Loop Alarm (Figs. 4.5 and 4.6)

Resistors (all 0.25 watt 5% carbon film)

R1	10k
R2	47k
R3	270R
R4	12k
R5	1M8
R6	5k6
R7	33k
R8	100k
R9	1M2
R10	12k
R11	33k

Capacitors

C1	100µ 16V elect
C2	4n7 polyester

C3	47n polyester
C4	100n polyester
C5	220n polyester
C6	100n polyester
C7	4n7 polyester

Semiconductors

IC1	TS555CN or similar
IC2	TS555CN or similar
IC3	TS555CN or similar
TR1	SFH350
TR2	BC549
TR3	BC549
D1	SFH750
D2	OA91
D3	OA91

Miscellaneous

LS1   Cased ceramic resonator

Case, circuit board, fibre-optic cable, 8 pin DIL IC holder (3 off), wire, solder, etc.

Opto R.P.M. Meter

Some r.p.m. meters use a form of electro-magnetic device to provide electrical pulses that can be measured by what is basically just a simple frequency meter circuit. An optical sensor is usually a more practical alternative if an add-on r.p.m. meter is required. The main advantage of an optical sensor is that it requires no major modifications to the motor, drill, or whatever. There is a further advantage in that an optical sensor has no moving parts, and does not wear out.

There are two basic approaches to optical r.p.m. sensing. The more simple of the two has a white mark on a dark coloured shaft, or a black mark on a light coloured shaft. The general idea is to have a photocell aimed at the shaft so that detects a change in light level each time the mark passes in front of it. This does, of course, occur once per revolution of the shaft, and the photocell therefore provides one pulse per revolution. The shaft must be reasonably well lit, and if

119

necessary a light source must be provided. The pulses from the photocell can be read using a frequency meter calibrated in terms of revolutions per minute. The alternative method of optical sensing is to arrange things so that a small bar protruding from the shaft passes between the photocell and a light source on each revolution of the shaft. Again, this produces a series of output pulses that can be read by a frequency meter circuit.

There are a couple of potential advantages in having the photocell situated in the main unit rather than near the shaft, with a fibre-optic cable to couple the pulses of light from the shaft to the photocell. One of these is that the fibre-optic cable is not susceptible to pick-up of electrical noise, whereas an electric cable from the photocell to the main unit could well pick up a certain amount of electrical interference. The other advantage is that a fibre-optic cable is capable of operating with a small shaft that is equipped with a very small mark. Without resorting to a fibre-optic cable it can be very difficult to get this system to operate reliably with small diameter shafts.

R.P.M. Circuit
The block diagram of Figure 4.7 helps to explain the way in which this r.p.m. meter functions. For the sake of compactness the fibre-optic cable or cables are not shown. The LED is only needed if the shaft would otherwise be in darkness, or in fairly dim conditions. I used the LED close to the shaft, but it would presumably be possible to have the LED in the main unit with a piece of fibre-optic cable being used to "pipe" the light to the shaft. At the input of the receiver section an amplifier boosts the output pulses from the photocell. They are then fed to a trigger circuit which provides strong enough pulses to drive the third stage, which is a monostable. In conjunction with a low-pass filter this provides a simple frequency to voltage conversion. A voltmeter at the output gives a reading directly in terms of r.p.m.

Figure 4.8 shows the circuit diagram for the fibre-optic r.p.m. meter. D1 is the LED, and this component (and R1) are only needed if the shaft would otherwise be inadequately lit. D1 should be an ultra-bright LED. The LED current is set at approximately 20 milliamps by R1, and this is sufficient to give

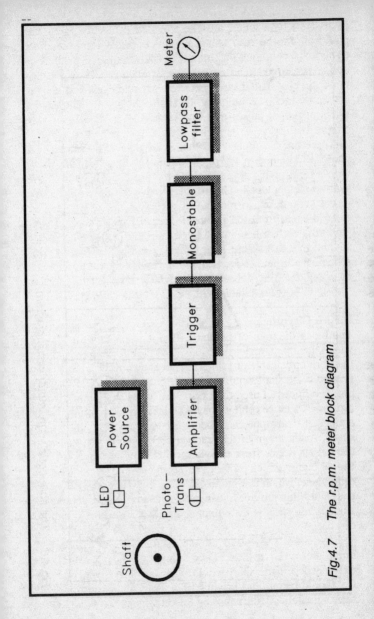

Fig.4.7   The r.p.m. meter block diagram

121

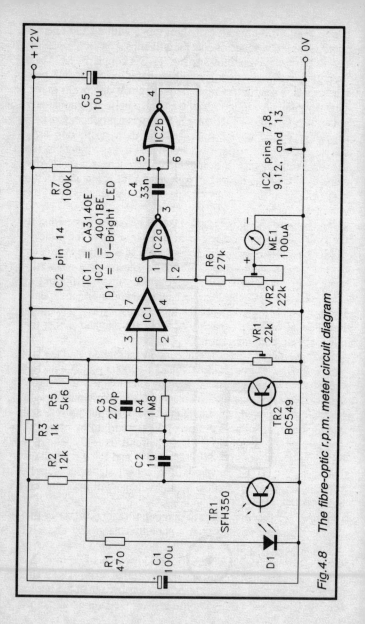

Fig. 4.8 The fibre-optic r.p.m. meter circuit diagram

IC1 = CA3140E
IC2 = 4001BE
D1 = U-Bright LED

IC2 pins 7, 8,
9, 12, and 13

IC2 pin 14

122

a high level of illumination at short range with a LED rated at about 2cd at a current flow of 20 milliamps.

The output from phototransistor TR1 is coupled by C2 to a high gain common emitter amplifier based on TR2. C3 provides a small amount of high frequency roll-off to this stage. This filtering aids good stability, and also helps to combat any noise on the input which might otherwise produce spurious triggering of the monostable. IC1 is used open loop as a simple clipping amplifier. VR1 provides a bias voltage to the non-inverting input of IC1, and effectively acts as a sensitivity control. The closer the wiper voltage of VR1 is matched to the bias voltage at TR2's collector, the higher the sensitivity of the circuit.

The monostable is a simple CMOS type that is essentially the same as the monostable circuits used in some of the projects described previously. ME1 is connected in a simple voltmeter circuit at the output of the monostable. Electronic lowpass filtering will not usually be needed since suitable filtering is effectively provided by the mechanical damping of the meter. If mechanical resonances of the meter cause "jitter" at certain frequencies, adding a capacitor of about 10μ in value across the meter should cure the problem.

VR2 enables the unit to be accurately calibrated, and the circuit is designed for a full scale value of 10000 r.p.m. Other full scale values can be accommodated by altering the values of R7 and (or) C4. For example, increasing C4 to 68n would roughly double the length of the monostable's output pulses, and would permit a full scale value of 5000 r.p.m. to be obtained. The current consumption of the circuit is only about 4 milliamps, or around 24 milliamps if D1 and R1 are included. The circuit must be powered from a well stabilised supply, because any variations in the supply voltage will upset the circuit's calibration.

Figure 4.9 shows the circuit diagram for an r.p.m. meter that uses a photodiode rather than a phototransistor. D2 and TR1 are used in a configuration that has been featured in several of the projects described previously. VR3 is given any setting that produces a reasonably strong output signal from TR1. This version of the circuit seems to be less sensitive than the phototransistor version. The phototransistor version is therefore

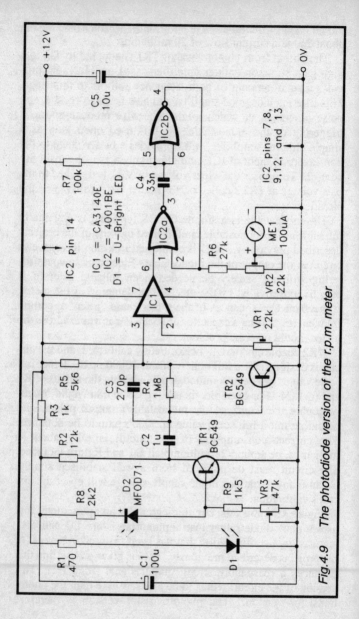

Fig.4.9 The photodiode version of the r.p.m. meter

IC1 = CA3140E
IC2 = 4001BE
D1 = U-Bright LED

IC2 pin 14

IC2 pins 7,8,
9,12, and 13

124

better if the system will use reflected light rather than the interrupted light method.

The CA3140E and 4001BE are both MOS integrated circuits, and require the standard anti-static handling precautions. With either version of the unit, VR1 is given any setting that gives reliable operation of the circuit. Setting the wiper voltage of VR1 very high or very low might result in inadequate sensitivity. This depends on the strength of the output signal from TR2. Adjusting VR1 towards a mid setting should give better sensitivity, but IC1 might produce a lot of spurious output pulses. It is a matter of using a bit of trial and error to find a satisfactory setting. Provided the output signal from TR2 is quite strong the precise setting of VR1 should not be too critical.

I found that the easiest way of calibrating the unit was to aim the end of the fibre-optic cable at a mains powered tungsten lamp. This produces a 100Hz "hum" signal from the photocell. 100Hz is the same frequency that is produced by a shaft rotating at 6000 r.p.m. ($100 \times 60 = 6000$). VR2 is simply adjusted for a reading of 60µA on ME1. It is not essential to recalibrate the meter's scale, since the current readings are easily converted into their equivalent r.p.m. values. Simply add two zeros to the current reading (e.g. 25µA corresponds to 2500 r.p.m.).

Machinery in operation, even small scale machinery, can be very dangerous, so observe all normal safety rules when installing this unit. In particular, do not work near any machine while it is actually in operation. Some experimentation will probably be needed in order to get a good signal from the photocell and reliable results from the meter, but I have usually found it to be reasonably easy to get units of this type working well.

Components for Opto R.P.M. Meter (Fig.4.8)

Resistors (all 0.25 watt 5% carbon film)
R1   470R
R2   12k
R3   1k
R4   1M8
R5   5k6

| R6 | 27k |
| R7 | 100k |

Potentiometers
| VR1 | 22k min preset |
| VR2 | 22k min preset |

Capacitors
C1	100µ 16V elect
C2	1µ polyester
C3	270p polystyrene
C4	33n polyester
C5	10µ 25V elect

Semiconductors
IC1	CA3140E
IC2	4001BE
TR1	SFH350
TR2	BC549
D1	Ultra-bright red LED

Miscellaneous
| ME1 | 100µA moving coil panel meter |

Case, circuit board, 8 pin DIL IC holder, 14 pin DIL IC holder, fibre-optic cable, wire, solder, etc.

Altered values and additional components (Fig. 4.9)
R8	2k2
R9	1k5
VR3	47k min preset
TR1	BC549
D2	MFOD71

Fibre-Optic Lamp

Last, and probably least, this project is a decorative table lamp which utilizes multi-core fibre-optic cable. No doubt many readers will have seen ready made lamps of this type, which are based on one or more pieces of multi-cored fibre-optic cable. Most of the sleeving is removed from the cable, and the fibres

126

cascade in fountain fashion from the top of the lamp. In ready-made units the fibres are normally illuminated via small bulbs and moving coloured filters operated by a small electric motor. This gives varying colours from the filaments, which produces an attractive and colourful display.

This do-it-yourself version is based on tricolour LEDs. There are two types of tricolour LED, and the more simple type is basically just red and green LED chips in the same encapsulation. A diffuser at the front of the component provides colour mixing so that a yellow/orange colour is produced with both of the LEDs switched on. By varying the relative intensities of the two LEDs, a range of colours from red through to green can be produced.

The second form of tricolour LED uses a more hi-tech approach, with the two LEDs on a single chip. With this type of LED the colour mixing occurs actually on the chip, and no diffuser is required. It is this second type of tricolour LED that is required for this project. Single chip Tricolour LEDs usually have clear plastic cases of the standard LED shape. The twin chip tricolour LEDs mainly have clear encapsulations, but are mostly non-standard shapes, with a flat front where the translucent diffusion screen can be seen.

The Circuit
Figures 4.10 and 4.11 show the circuit diagram for the fibre-optic lamp. The basic action of the circuit is to vary the brightness of one section of the LED at a very low rate of about 0.2Hz (one cycle every five seconds), and to vary the brightness of the second section at a slightly higher rate of about 0.4Hz (one cycle every 2.5 seconds). This gives a varying phase relationship between the two halves of the LED, which in turn gives varying colour and intensity from the LED.

The circuit consists of two virtually identical triangular/squarewave oscillators of the type which uses an integrator driving a trigger circuit. In this case it is only the triangular output signals from the integrators that are required. Each oscillator drive one section of the LED via an emitter follower buffer stage and a current limiting resistor. The latter gives a maximum LED current of about 30 milliamps. This is sufficient to give a reasonably high light output level from a

127

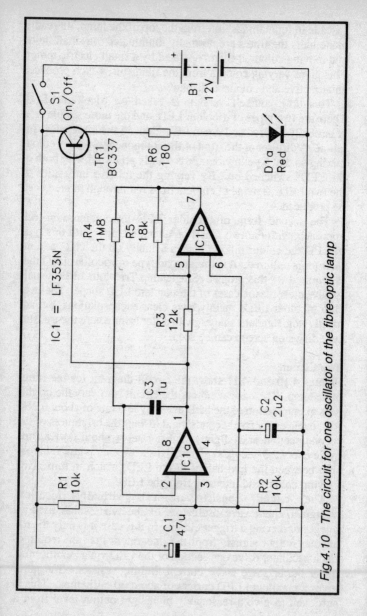

Fig.4.10 The circuit for one oscillator of the fibre-optic lamp

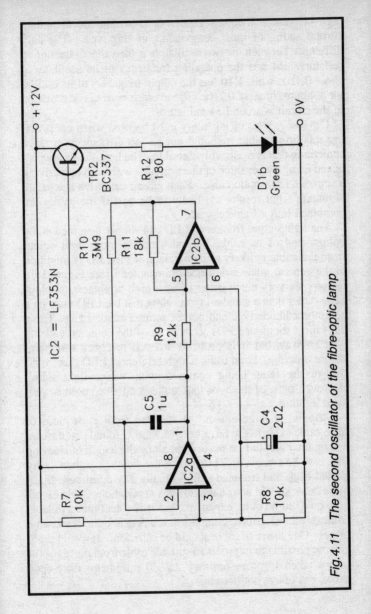

Fig.4.11 The second oscillator of the fibre-optic lamp

high brightness tricolour LED, but is within the maximum current rating of most components of this type. The only difference between the two oscillators is the value of the timing resistors. R4 sets the operating frequency of its oscillator at about 0.4Hz, while R10 sets the output frequency of its oscillator at approximately 0.2Hz. The average current consumption of the circuit is around 34 milliamps.

Obviously a bit of ingenuity must be used when constructing this project, but it should not be too difficult to produce something that is reasonably passable. The best results are produced using two or three of these circuits with each one driving a separate fibre-optic cable. Each circuit can drive a separate "fountain", but results are likely to be best if the cables are combined into a single cascade.

The light output from each LED can simply be aimed at the bottom end of its cable, but substantially more light output from the cable is likely to be obtained if the LED is modified in the general manner described in chapter 1 (see Figure 1.6). Results are very much better using a high brightness tricolour LED rather than a standard type. Note that the LED must be a common cathode type and not a common anode LED. These days most tricolour LEDs seem to be of the common cathode type anyway, but it is probably as well to check this point before ordering. Even using a high brightness LED there is no risk of the lamp being confused with a laser-light show! However, units of this type look quite good when used in subdued lighting.

Stripping a large amount of sleeving from each piece of fibre-optic cable might be rather awkward. I found that the easiest method was to first make a slit along the length of sleeving that is to be removed. This part of the sleeving is then easily peeled back and trimmed off. Virtually any multi-core fibre-optic cable should be suitable for this application. Cable of this type tends to be quite expensive, but it is sometimes available from surplus electronic component retailers at quite reasonable prices. One metre of cable should be sufficient. It would probably be possible to improvise a suitable cable from pieces of filament taken from an ordinary 2.2/1.0 millimetre fibre-optic cable, but I have not tried this.

Components for Fibre-Optic Lamp (Figs.4.10 and 4.11)

Resistors (all 0.25 watt 5% carbon film)
R1	10k
R2	10k
R3	12k
R4	1M8
R5	18k
R6	180R
R7	10k
R8	10k
R9	12k
R10	3M9
R11	18k
R12	180R

Capacitors
C1	47µ 16V elect
C2	2µ2 50V elect
C3	1µ polyester
C4	2µ2 50V elect
C5	1µ polyester

Semiconductors
IC1	LF353N
IC2	LF353N
TR1	BC337
TR2	BC337
D1	Tricolour common cathode high brightness LED

Miscellaneous
S1	s.p.s.t. min toggle
B1	12V (8 × HP7 size cells in holder)

Case, circuit board, 8 pin DIL IC holder (2 off), multi-core fibre-optic cable, PP3 type battery connector, wire, solder, etc.

Notes

133

Please note following is a list of other titles that are available in our range of Radio, Electronics and Computer books.

These should be available from all good Booksellers, Radio Component Dealers and Mail Order Companies.

However, should you experience difficulty in obtaining any title in your area, then please write directly to the Publisher enclosing payment to cover the cost of the book plus adequate postage.

If you would like a complete catalogue of our entire range of Radio, Electronics and Computer Books then please send a Stamped Addressed Envelope to:

BERNARD BABANI (publishing) LTD
THE GRAMPIANS
SHEPHERDS BUSH ROAD
LONDON W6 7NF
ENGLAND